Exploring Creation
with
Physical Science

Exploring Creation with Physical Science
Student Notebook

Published by Apologia Science,
a division of Apologia Educational Ministries, Inc.
1106 Meridian Plaza, Suite 220/340
Anderson, Indiana 46016
www.apologia.com

Manufactured in the USA
Sixth Printing: April 2016

ISBN: 978-1-935495-71-0

Text: Vicki Dincher

Portions of this notebook are taken directly from
Exploring Creation with Physical Science, 2nd edition,
authored by Jay Wile and published by Apologia Educational Ministries, Inc.

Book Design: Doug Powell

Printed by Bang Printing, Brainerd, MN

Table of Contents

PARENT NOTES

The text contains 16 modules, and this notebook contains 16 corresponding modules. Each module in this notebook provides graphic organizers designed to reinforce the material presented in the text, with an emphasis on scientific vocabulary. Each module in the notebook also provides space for students to answer the "On Your Own" questions, study guide questions, and summary questions, creating a concise handbook to study for the module and quarterly tests. The fill-in-the-blank summaries are strictly optional. If students are having trouble studying for the test, you may choose to assign the summaries for extra practice. If students have mastered the material, they may skip the summaries and take the test after reviewing the module in the text and notebook. The tests and the answers to the study guides, summaries, and tests are provided in the *Solutions and Tests for Exploring Creation with Physical Science* manual.

The notebook also contains lab report forms for every experiment in each module. Students can simply complete the lab report forms as they are investigating each experiment when they come to it in the text. Finally, the notebook provides "Digging Deeper" and "What Does God's Word Say" opportunities throughout the modules. The "What Does God's Word Say" sections direct students to Scripture to investigate some aspect of the module. The "Digging Deeper" sections provide hands-on or web-based activities to discover more about a given topic in the module. Website URLs are provided in each "Digging Deeper" section, or you can access all of the URLs for this notebook at link.apologia.com/ECPS2N.

About Experiments

Completing hands-on lab investigations is an essential part of science education. Experimenting provides students with a unique opportunity to engage in the processes of inquiry and exploration as they manipulate equipment and materials to construct their knowledge of scientific concepts and phenomena. However, experiments can be time consuming, especially if the needed materials must be gathered first. To make completing experiments as students come to them in each module more convenient, I suggest that you put together a lab box to contain all of the materials required for the experiments in each module. This can be done several ways:

- During the summer, gather all non-perishable items and place them into the box (or a couple of boxes). Tape a list of the perishable items required for each module to the top of the boxes. This works best for my family.

- Four times during the year, gather the non-perishable items needed for the next four modules and tape a list of the perishable items required for these modules to the top of the box.

- Before each module, put away the materials for the previous module and gather the new materials. In most cases, the perishable items can be gathered at this time too.

You can find a list of materials for each module in Appendix C of the text (page 481). Instructions for completing a lab report are in the experiment section of this notebook. A checklist and a grading rubric are in Appendix A of this notebook. You may wish to copy the checklist so students can refer to it when completing each lab report.

Daily Schedule

The 16 modules of the text have been broken down into daily lessons on the schedule below. Following this schedule will enable students to complete the text in 34 weeks, working approximately 30 minutes to 1 hour per day, depending on whether there is an experiment. The schedule provides students with a clear indication of what should be covered each day and a place to check off what they've accomplished.

WEEK	DAY 1	DAY 2
1	**Module 1 – The Basics** Read pp. 1–7 in text Experiment 1.1 Notebook (NB) pp. 11–12	Read pp. 7–9 in text NB pp. 12–13
2	Study guide questions 1–9 on NB pp. 18–20	Study guide questions 10–14 on NB pp. 20–21
3	Read pp. 28–32 in text Experiment 2.2 NB pp. 24–25	Read pp. 32–36 in text Experiment 2.3 NB pp. 25–27
4	Study guide questions 1–10 on NB pp. 32–33	Study guide questions 11–20 on NB pp. 33–34
5	Read pp. 60–61 in text NB pp. 36–37	Read pp. 62–65 in text NB pp. 38–39
6	Study guide questions 1–5 on NB pp. 43–46	Study guide questions 6–17 on NB pp. 46–47
7	Read pp. 85–86 in text NB p. 49	Read pp. 86–89 in text Experiment 4.2 NB pp. 50–51
8	Read pp. 99–101 in text Experiment 4.6 NB pp. 55–56	Study guide questions 1–5 on NB pp. 56–58

The Daily Schedule for the Physical Science full course CD is available at apologia.com/bookextras
Password: Physicalcreation

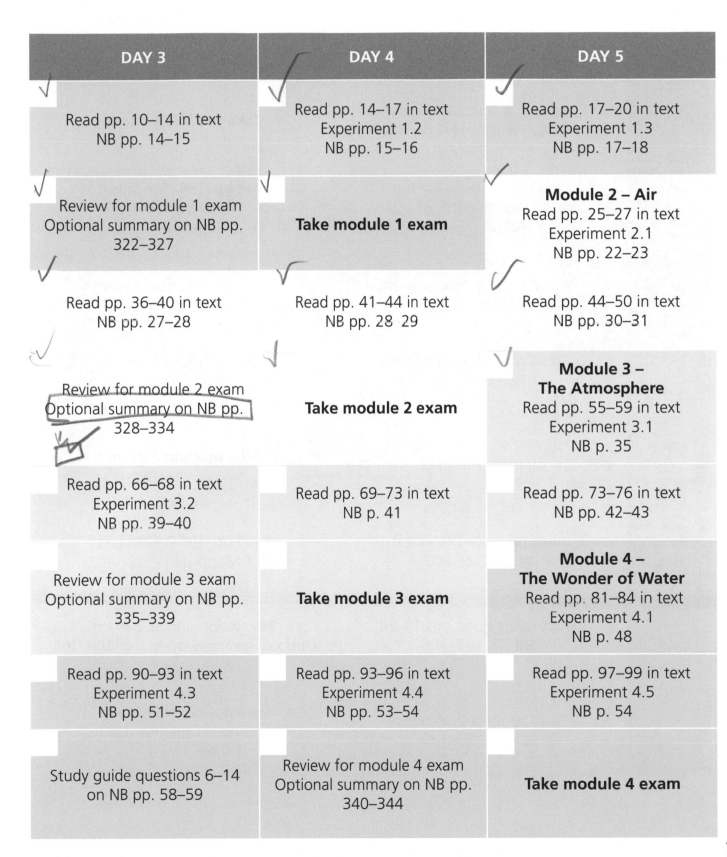

DAY 3	DAY 4	DAY 5
Read pp. 10–14 in text NB pp. 14–15	Read pp. 14–17 in text Experiment 1.2 NB pp. 15–16	Read pp. 17–20 in text Experiment 1.3 NB pp. 17–18
Review for module 1 exam Optional summary on NB pp. 322–327	**Take module 1 exam**	**Module 2 – Air** Read pp. 25–27 in text Experiment 2.1 NB pp. 22–23
Read pp. 36–40 in text NB pp. 27–28	Read pp. 41–44 in text NB pp. 28 29	Read pp. 44–50 in text NB pp. 30–31
Review for module 2 exam Optional summary on NB pp. 328–334	**Take module 2 exam**	**Module 3 – The Atmosphere** Read pp. 55–59 in text Experiment 3.1 NB p. 35
Read pp. 66–68 in text Experiment 3.2 NB pp. 39–40	Read pp. 69–73 in text NB p. 41	Read pp. 73–76 in text NB pp. 42–43
Review for module 3 exam Optional summary on NB pp. 335–339	**Take module 3 exam**	**Module 4 – The Wonder of Water** Read pp. 81–84 in text Experiment 4.1 NB p. 48
Read pp. 90–93 in text Experiment 4.3 NB pp. 51–52	Read pp. 93–96 in text Experiment 4.4 NB pp. 53–54	Read pp. 97–99 in text Experiment 4.5 NB p. 54
Study guide questions 6–14 on NB pp. 58–59	Review for module 4 exam Optional summary on NB pp. 340–344	**Take module 4 exam**

WEEK	DAY 1	DAY 2
9	**Take quarterly test 1**	**Module 5 – The Hydrosphere** Read pp. 105–109 in text NB p. 60
10	Read pp. 120–121 in text NB pp. 65–66	Read pp. 122–126 in text Experiment 5.3 NB p. 66
11	Review for module 5 exam Optional summary on NB pp. 345–349	**Take module 5 exam**
12	Read pp. 138–144 in text Experiment 6.3 NB pp. 75–76	Read pp. 144–148 in text Experiment 6.4 NB pp. 76–77
13	Study guide questions 8–24 on NB pp. 81–84	Review for module 6 exam Optional summary on NB pp. 350–354
14	Read pp. 165–169 in text NB pp. 88–89	Read pp. 170–171 in text NB pp. 89–90
15	Review for module 7 exam Optional summary on NB pp. 355–359	**Take module 7 exam**
16	Read pp. 190–194 in text NB pp. 99–100	Read pp. 194–197 in text NB pp. 101–102
17	Study guide questions 14–24 NB pp. 103–106	Review for module 8 exam Optional summary on NP pp. 360–364
18	Read pp. 206–208 in text NB pp. 108–109	Read pp. 208–212 in text Complete Experiment 9.1 NB pp. 110–111

DAY 3	DAY 4	DAY 5
Read pp. 109–113 in text Experiment 5.1 NB pp. 61–62	Read pp. 113–116 in text NB pp. 62–64	Read pp. 116–120 in text Experiment 5.2 NB pp. 64–65
Read pp. 126–127 in text NB p.67	Study guide questions 1–7 on NB pp. 67–69	Study guide questions 8–21 on NB pp. 69–71
Module 6 – Earth & the Lithosphere: Read pp. 131–133 in text NB pp. 72–73	Read pp. 133–136 in text Experiment 6.1 NB p. 73	Read pp. 136–137 in text Experiment 6.2 NB pp. 73–74
Read pp. 148–151 in text NB pp. 77–78	Read pp. 151–153 in text NB p. 79	Study guide questions 1–7 on NB pp. 79–81
Take module 6 exam	**Module 7 – Factors That Affect Earth's Weather** Read pp. 157–160 in text NB pp. 85–86	Read pp. 160–165 in text Start Experiment 7.1 NB pp. 86–87
Read pp. 172–176 in text NB pp. 91–92	Study guide questions 1–7 on NB pp. 92–94	Study guide questions 8–20 on NB pp. 94–95
Module 8 – Weather & Its Prediction Read pp. 181–183 in text NB pp. 96–97	Read pp. 183–186 in text NB p. 98	Read pp. 186–189 in text Start Experiment 8.1 NB pp. 98–99
Read p. 198 in text Experiment 7.1 NB p. 102	Read p. 199 in text Experiment 8.2 NB p. 102	Study guide questions 1–13 on NB pp. 102–103
Take module 8 exam	**Take quarterly test 2**	**Module 9 – An Intro to the Physics of Motion** Read pp. 203–205 in text NB pp. 107–108
Read pp. 212–218 in text NB pp. 111–114	Read pp. 218–221 in text Complete Experiment 9.2 NB p. 114	Read pp. 221–223 in text Complete Experiment 9.3 NB pp. 114–115

WEEK	DAY 1	DAY 2
19	Study guide questions 1–7 NB pp. 115–117	Study guide questions 8–17 NB pp. 118–120
20	Read pp. 234–237 in text Experiment 10.2 NB pp. 122–123	Read pp. 237–240 in text Experiment 10.3 NB pp. 123–124
21	Study guide questions 1–7 on NB pp. 129–131	Study guide questions 8–17 on NB pp. 131–133
22	Read pp. 260–263 in text Experiment 11.1 NB p. 136	Read pp. 263–265 in text NB p. 137
23	Read pp. 276–280 in text Experiment 11.3 NB p. 142	Study guide questions 1–12 on NB pp. 142–145
24	**Module 12 – Forces in Creation—Part 2** Read pp. 285–289 in text Experiment 12.1 NB pp. 147–148	Read pp. 290–291 in text NB p. 149
25	Read pp. 302–304 in text NB pp. 153–154	Read pp. 305–308 in text NB pp. 154–156
26	**Take module 12 exam**	**Take quarterly test 3**
27	Read pp. 325–326 in text NB pp. 163–165	Read pp. 327–329 in text NB pp. 165–167
28	Study guide questions 7–20 on NB pp. 170–172	Review for module 13 exam Optional summary on NB pp. 388–393

DAY 3	DAY 4	DAY 5
Review for module 9 exam Optional summary on NB pp. 365–370	**Take module 9 exam**	**Module 10 – Newton's Laws** Read pp. 229–234 in text Experiment 10.1 NB p. 121
Read pp. 240–244 in text NB pp. 124–125	Read pp. 244–246 in text NB pp. 126–127	Read pp. 246–249 in text Experiment 10.4 NB pp. 128–129
Review for module 10 exam Optional summary on NB pp. 371–375	**Take module 10 exam**	**Module 11 – Forces in Creation—Part 1** Read pp. 255–259 in text NB pp. 134–136
Read pp. 265–269 in text NB pp. 138–139	Read pp. 269–273 in text NB pp. 139–141	Read pp. 274–276 in text Experiment 11.2 NB p. 141
Study guide questions 13–23 on NB pp. 145–146	Review for module 11 exam Optional summary on NB pp. 376–381	**Take module 11 exam**
Read pp. 291–295 in text Experiment 12.2 NB pp. 149–150	Read pp. 295–299 in text NB pp. 150–152	Read pp. 299–301 in text Experiment 12.3 NB pp. 152–153
Study guide questions 1–10 on NB pp. 156–158	Study guide questions 11–20 on NB pp. 158–159	Review for module 12 exam Optional summary on NB pp. 382–387
Module 13 – Forces in Creation—Part 3 Read pp. 313–316 in text NB p. 160	Read pp. 317–319 in text NB pp. 161–162	Read pp. 320–325 in text NB pp. 162–163
Read pp. 330–331 in text NB pp. 167–168	Read pp. 332–336 in text NB p. 168	Study guide questions 1–6 on NB pp. 168–170
Take module 13 exam	**Module 14 – Waves & Sound** Read pp. 341–344 in text NB pp. 173–174	Read pp. 344–347 in text Experiment 14.1 NB p. 175

WEEK	DAY 1	DAY 2
29	Read pp. 347–350 in text Experiment 14.2 NB pp. 175–176	Read pp. 351–352 in text NB pp. 177–178
30	Study guide questions 1–7 on NB pp. 182–184	Study guide questions 8–19 on NB pp. 185–187
31	Read pp. 370–374 in text Experiment 15.1 NB pp. 189–190	Read pp. 374–377 in text Experiment 15.2 NB pp. 190–191
32	Read pp. 389–392 in text NB pp. 195–196	Study guide questions 1–21 NB pp. 196–200
33	Read pp. 401–404 in text NB pp. 202–204	Read pp. 404–409 in text NB pp. 204–206
34	Study guide questions 1–11 on NB pp. 210–212	Study guide questions 12–25 on NB pp. 213–214

DAY 3	DAY 4	DAY 5
Read pp. 353–355 in text NB pp. 178–180. Complete Experiment 14.3	Read pp. 355–357 in text Experiment 14.4 NB pp. 180–181	Read pp. 357–362 in text Experiment 14.5 NB pp. 181–182
Review for module 14 exam Optional summary on NB pp. 394–399	**Take module 14 exam**	**Module 15 – Light** Read pp. 367–370 in text NB pp. 188–189
Read pp. 377–383 in text Experiments 15.3 & 15.4 NB pp. 191–192	Read pp. 383–385 in text NB p. 193	Read pp. 385–389 in text Experiment 15.5 NB p. 194
Review for module 15 exam Optional summary on NB pp. 400–405	**Take module 15 exam**	**Module 16 – An Introduction to Astrophysics** Read pp. 397–401 in text NB pp. 201–202
Read pp. 409–411 in text NB pp. 206–207	Read pp. 411–413 in text NB pp. 207–208	Read pp. 413–418 in text Experiment 16.1 NB pp. 209–210
Review for module 16 exam Optional summary on NB pp. 406–410	**Take module 16 exam**	**Take quarterly test 4**

STUDENT NOTES

This notebook will help you organize your notes, provide a space to answer all of the module questions, and serve as your lab notebook. When you are finished with the *Exploring Creation with Physical Science* course, this notebook will be a great reference book and resource as you study these science concepts in more depth in the future.

You should begin this course by becoming familiar with your text and this notebook. The daily schedule on pages 2–9 breaks down each module into approximately two weeks of work. You can check off each day as you complete the work outlined as a way of recording just how far you've come in your study of God's amazing creation.

About Experiments

Completing experiments and lab reports is an essential part of science education. The experiment section in the back of this notebook contains a lab report form for every experiment you will do as you read the text. Read the instructions for completing a lab report in the experiment section of this notebook just before you start your first experiment. You may wish to make a copy of the checklist in Appendix A so that you can have it in front of you when completing each lab report.

Collect all of the materials that you will need to complete all of the experiments in each module before you start the module, and keep them in a box designated just for your lab materials. That way you will have everything you need when you need it. This will save you a lot of time in the long run. You can find a list of materials needed for each module on page 481 in the text.

The Basics

Introduction & Atoms and Molecules

Read pages 1–7 in the text. To help you remember the new information you will learn as you read, explain what elements, atoms, molecules, and compounds are in the graphic organizer below.

Complete experiment 1.1 and fill out the lab report. Then answer "On Your Own" questions 1.1–1.2.

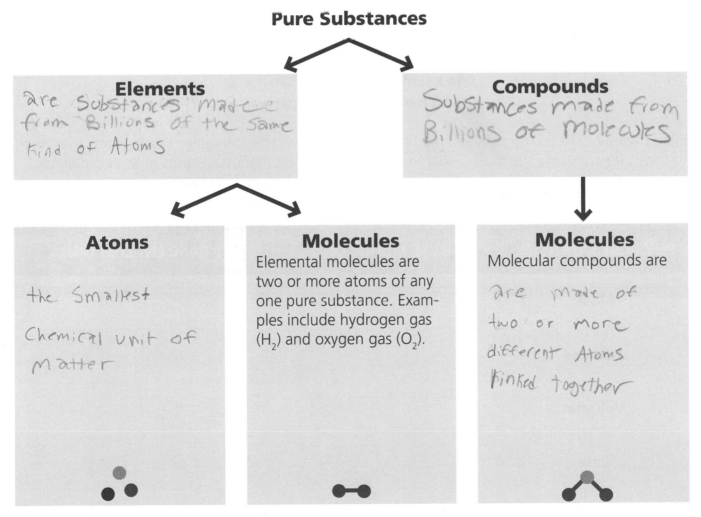

Pure Substances

Elements

are substances made from Billions of the same Kind of Atoms

Compounds

Substances made from Billions of molecules

Atoms

the Smallest Chemical unit of Matter

Molecules

Elemental molecules are two or more atoms of any one pure substance. Examples include hydrogen gas (H_2) and oxygen gas (O_2).

Molecules

Molecular compounds are

are made of two or more different Atoms Kinked together

ON YOUR OWN

1.1 A molecule is broken down into its constituent atoms. Do these atoms have the same properties as the molecule? Atoms do not have the same Properties as a molecule because when Atoms Hink together, the molecule they make will Have completly different properties.

ON YOUR OWN

1.2 When salt is dissolved in water, it actually breaks down, into two different substances. Is salt composed of atoms or molecules?

Salt is composed of moleculs

Measurement and Units & The Metric System

Read pages 7–9 in the text. As you read about the different physical quantities scientists may need to measure, complete the table below to help you remember their base units in both the metric and English systems. Afterwards, you can learn about the history of measurement and what God's Word has to say about measuring by completing the following activities.

PHYSICAL QUANTITY	BASE METRIC UNIT	BASE ENGLISH UNIT
Mass	gram	Slug
Distance	meter	foot
Volume	liter	gallon
Time	Seconds	Seconds

DIGGING DEEPER
The History of Measurement and Metrics

If you'd like to know more about how people have measured things through the ages, as well as how the metric system was developed, check out the following website. Very interesting!

link.apologia.com/ECPS2N/1.1

Write in the space below one fact that you didn't know before you looked up this website.

_____

_____

_____

_____

_____

WHAT DOES GOD'S WORD SAY?

The Bible talks about measuring! Look up the following scripture and write down what God tells us to measure or number and why.

Psalm 90:12

_____

_____

_____

_____

_____

_____

_____

Manipulating Units &
Converting between Units

Read pages 10–14 in the text, paying careful attention to example 1.1. If you still need more help with manipulating and converting units, look up the video at the following website.

link.apologia.com/ECPS2N/1.2

Then answer "On Your Own" questions 1.3–1.5, making sure to show all your work.

ON YOUR OWN

1.3 A student measures the mass of a book as 12,321 g. what is the book's mass in kg?   the Book was

12.32 Kg

$$1g = 0.001 Kg =$$

$$\frac{12,321 g}{1} \times \frac{0.001 Kg}{1 g} =$$

12.321

ON YOUR OWN

1.4 If a glass contains 0.121 L of milk, what is the volume of milk in mL?

the glass of milk Volume is

121.0 mL

ON YOUR OWN

1.5 In the National Basketball Association (NBA), the distance from the three-point line to the basket is 723.9 cm at the top of the arc. What is this distance in meters?

7.239 meters or m

Converting between Systems

Read pages 14–17 in the text, paying careful attention to example 1.2. As you read, complete the table below to help you remember the relationship between the English and metric systems. Complete "On Your Own" questions 1.6–1.8, showing all your work. Then complete experiment 1.2 and fill out the lab report.

MEASUREMENT	ENGLISH/METRIC RELATIONSHIP
Distance	Meter or foot
Mass	Gram Slug
Volume	litir Gallon

ON YOUR OWN

1.6 A piece of yarn is 3.00 inches long. How many centimeters long is it?

Dont Know how many inches in centimeter

ON YOUR OWN

1.7 How many slugs are there in 12 kg?

Dont Know how many slugs in 1 kg

ON YOUR OWN

1.8 If an object occupies 3.2 gallons of space, how many liters of space does it occupy?

Dont Know how many liters in gallon

Concentration

Read pages 17–20 in the text. Complete experiment 1.3 and fill out the lab report. Use the space below to explain the scientific term "concentration" in your own words. Then answer "On Your Own" questions 1.9–1.10.

Concentration _is the quantity of substance within a certain volume_

ON YOUR OWN

1.9 Muriatic acid is sold in hardware stores for use in cleaning. Pool owners, for example, use it to clean hard water stains and algae stains from their pools. Its active ingredient is hydrochloric acid. The Works is a toilet bowl cleaner with hydrochloric acid as its active ingredient. There are approximately 350 grams of hydrochloric acid in a liter of muriatic acid, and there are approximately 30 grams of hydrochloric acid in a liter of The Works. why is muriatic acid a more powerful cleaner than The Works? _muriatic acid is more powerfull because the hydrochloric acid is more concentrated. It has 350 g of hydrochloric acid wereas a liter of the works has only 30 grams._

ON YOUR OWN

1.10 Sodium (so' dee uhm) is a necessary part of a healthy diet. If a person does not ingest enough sodium every day, that person will get sick and perhaps die. Nevertheless, some people try to limit their sodium intake by eating a low-salt diet. How can it be good to limit your sodium intake, even though sodium is a necessary part of body chemistry? because if you take to much sodium it becoums so concentrated it will be Toxic to your body.

Complete the study guide questions and have your parent correct them. If you need additional practice, you may wish to complete the optional summary for this module, located in the summary section at the back of this notebook. Take time to understand anything that you may have missed and review your notes before taking the test for this module.

Study Guide

1 Write out the definitions for the following terms:

a. Atom *Smallest chemical unit of matter*

b. Molecule *made of 2 or more Atoms to make a substance with unique properties.*

c. Concentration *quantity of substance within a certain volum*

2 Fifty grams of a carbon disulfide can be broken down into 42.1 grams of sulfur and 7.9 grams of carbon. Is carbon disulfide made up of atoms or molecules?

Carbon disulfide is made of molecules

3 If you put iron near a magnet, the iron will be attracted to the magnet. Rust is made up of molecules that contain iron atoms and oxygen atoms. Rust is not attracted to a magnet. If rust contains iron atoms, and iron is attracted to a magnet, why isn't rust attracted to a magnet?

Because when you combine oxygen atoms and Iron atoms you get molecules with unique properties

4 A statue is made out of copper and displayed outside. After many years, what color will the statue be?

it will be green because the copper atoms react with the water and carbon dioxide in the air to make hydroxycarbonate

5 Have scientists actually seen atoms?

No scientists use the scanning tunneling electron microscope to make calculations with a theory called quantum mechanics

6 Give the numerical meaning for the prefixes "centi," "milli," and "kilo."

centi _0.01_   kilo _1000_

milli _0.001_

19

7 If you wanted to measure an object's mass, what metric unit would you use? What English unit would you use?

metric unit ___gram___   English unit ___slugs___

8 If you wanted to measure an object's volume, what metric unit would you use? What English unit would you use?

metric unit ___liter___   English unit ___gallon___

9 If you wanted to measure an object's length, what metric unit would you use? What English unit would you use?

metric unit ___meter___   English unit ___foot___

10 How many centimeters are in 1.3 meters?

1 cm = 100 meters

1.30 x 100 = 130cm are in 1.3 meters

11 If a person has a mass of 75 kg, what is his or her mass in grams?

1 kg = 1000 g.

75 x 1000

150000 g

12 How many liters of milk are in 0.500 gallons of milk? (1 gal = 3.78 L)

0.50
x 3.78
4.00
35.00
150.00
189.0

0.500 x 3.78 =   L

13 A meterstick is 100.0 centimeters long. How long is it in inches? (1 in = 2.54 cm)

$100. \, cm \div 2.54 \, cm$ $\frac{2.54}{100}$ $\frac{254}{100}$

$100 \cdot \frac{100}{254}$ $\frac{10000}{254}$ $\begin{array}{r} 254 \\ \times \ 3 \\ \hline 762 \end{array}$

14 Ozone is a poisonous gas that can build up in the air in dense cities. Thus, there are many environmental initiatives to lower the amount of ozone in the air we breathe. One way you can make ozone, however, is by baking bread. The nice smell you associate with baking bread is actually due, in part, to ozone. If ozone is poisonous, why is baking bread not considered a dangerous activity?

the ozone concentraicinor is to Low to be Dangerous,

Air

Introduction & The Air and Humidity

Read pages 25–27 in the text. To help you remember the new information you will learn as you read, explain what humidity, absolute humidity, and relative humidity are in the spaces below. Complete experiment 2.1 and fill out the lab report. Then answer "On Your Own" questions 2.1–2.2.

Humidity

The Moisture content of air

Absolute Humidity

The mass of water vaper contained in a certain volume of Air, or is a measure of the concentraintion of vaper in the air

Relative Humidity

The ratio of the mass of water vapor in the air at a given temperature to the maximum mass of water vaper the air could hold at that temperature, expressed as a percentage.

ON YOUR OWN

2.1 Suppose you left a glass of water outside on two different days. On the first day, it is warm and humid. On the second day, it is the same temperature, but the humidity is low. Each day, you measure how long it takes the water to completely evaporate from the glass. On which day will the time it takes the water to evaporate be the smallest?

On the Scconed day.

ON YOUR OWN

2.2 Suppose you did the same experiment that was described in question 2.1 when the relative humidity was 100%. How quickly would the water evaporate from the glass? probably extremly slowly. or it would not evaborate.

The Composition of Air

Read pages 28–32 in the text. Complete the graphic organizer below by listing all of the gases that make up dry air. Make sure to include their percentages. Complete experiment 2.2 and fill out the lab report. You will be using matches, so you should ask a parent for help. Make sure you practice putting the balloon on the bottle before starting the experiment. Place your bottle in a 9"x13" baking pan to keep the mess to a minimum. Then answer "On Your Own" questions 2.3–2.4.

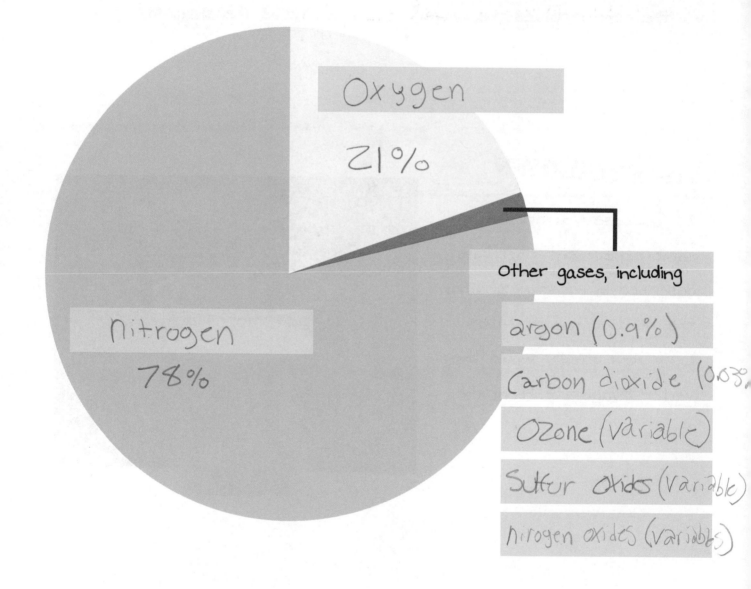

Oxygen 21%

nitrogen 78%

Other gases, including

argon (0.9%)

Carbon dioxide (0.03%)

Ozone (variable)

Sulfur Oxides (variable)

nitrogen oxides (variable)

ON YOUR OWN

2.3 If a scientist were to measure the percentages of nitrogen and oxygen in a sample of air that was not dry, would they be greater than, less than, or essentially the same as the percentages shown in figure 2.1? Probably less because you just add Humidity to the mix and so the Percentages goes down. (rain)

ON YOUR OWN

2.4 At high altitudes, there is less air around you as compared to lower altitudes. Would a candle at high altitudes burn dimmer, brighter, or essentially the same as a candle at low altitudes?

dimmer because there is less oxygen in the air to make the chemical reaction between oxygen and wood molecules wood.

Carbon Dioxide in the Air

Read pages 32–36 in the text. Complete experiment 2.3 and fill out the lab report. If you have two thermometers, you can set up both parts of the experiment at the same time. Find out more about the greenhouse effect by completing the "Digging Deeper" activity. Then answer "On Your Own" questions 2.5–2.6.

DIGGING DEEPER
The Greenhouse Effect

Check out the following link about the greenhouse effect and then explain why Earth is "just right," using the Goldilocks principle. Why is Venus too hot and Mercury too cold? What does that tell you about God, who placed the planets and the stars in the sky?

link.apologia.com/ECPS2N/2.1

Write one fact that you didn't know before you looked up this website.

Green House gass
H_2O, CO_2, N_2O, CH_4

ON YOUR OWN

2.5 we know that if the carbon dioxide concentration were too low, plants would starve. conversely, experiments indicate that many plants actually flourish when the concentration of carbon dioxide in their vicinity increases. How can this fact help explain why some experiments indicate that houseplants tend to grow better when their caretakers talk to them? because when their caretakers talk to them the carbon dioxide comes out of their body onto the plant helping photosythosis.

ON YOUR OWN

2.6 we know that our bodies do not use the nitrogen we inhale. Nevertheless, in figure 2.5, notice that the percentage of nitrogen in exhaled air is lower than the percentage of nitrogen in inhaled air. If our bodies do not use nitrogen in any way, why does the percentage decrease? because, when you breath out, you add more to the mix that you breath in, therefore causing the percentage to decrease, not the amount.

Global Warming

Read pages 36–40 in the text. Use the space below to explain why personal experience may not be a reliable method of determining the occurrence of global warming. Also briefly explain what the author wanted you to learn from the graphs in figures 2.6 and 2.7. Then answer "On Your Own" question 2.7.

in the graphs 2.6 and 2.7, the Author wanted me to learn is to always look at the y axis and the X axis, because the X axis in 2.6 was a very tiny range of tempurature compared to the 2.7s y axis tempurature range. this exercise wants me to state why personal experience is not reliable as a method of determining global warming, but instead I will state reasons why global warming is happening or going to happen, first, in the reading i did, the Author did say there was a slight tempurature change in the world, although this was slight it still happened, after a long time this could result in Global warming.

there is know proof of Global warming, Pluse Golobal weirmay is not just the increase in tempurature it is also the Polllusion on the Air. (x)

27

ON YOUR OWN

2.7 One popular thing to do in American politics is to note that many of the past few years have been some of the warmest ever recorded. This is then used to support the idea that global warming is happening. What is wrong with this kind of argument?

number one, the global tempurture in the Middle ages where warner then temperatures know. Second, you have to use long term data to know if there is global warming because global warming is a Long term effect.

Parts Per Million & Ozone

Read pages 41–44 in the text, paying careful attention to example 2.1. As you read, use the drawing below to explain how ozone in the ozone layer is beneficial to life on earth. Then answer "On Your Own" questions 2.8–2.10.

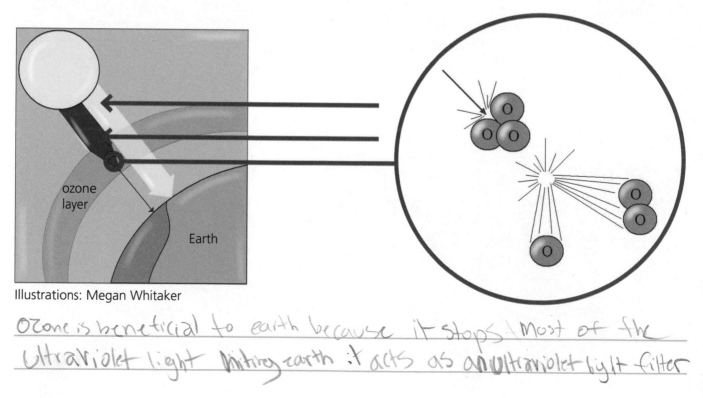

Illustrations: Megan Whitaker

Ozone is beneficial to earth because it stops most of the ultraviolet light hitting earth it acts as an ultraviolet light filter

ON YOUR OWN

2.8 The concentration of argon in the air is about 0.9%. What is this in ppm?

$$\frac{0.9\%}{1} = \frac{10,000 \text{ ppm}}{1\%}$$

$$\boxed{9000.0 \text{ ppm}}$$

ON YOUR OWN

2.9 convert 11 ppm into percent.

$$\frac{11 \text{ ppm}}{1} = \frac{1\%}{10,000 \text{ ppm}}$$

$$\frac{11}{10,000} \quad \boxed{0.0011\%}$$

ON YOUR OWN

2.10 One evolutionary theory of how life originated on the planet requires that, at one point, there was no oxygen in the atmosphere. This theory, of course, assumes that the first life form did not breathe oxygen. Since there are organisms today that can exist without breathing oxygen, this is not as fantastic as it may first sound. Based on what you learned in this section, however, what serious objection can you raise against the theory that life originated on an earth with no oxygen in its air? because to have life you must have an ozone layer to filter out ultraviolet light from the sun but you cant have that if ther is no oxygen because ozone is made out of 3 oxygen atoms.

Air Pollution

Read pages 44–50 in the text. As you read, use the graphic organizer below to record how scientists and the U.S. government have developed ways to decrease air pollutants over the last 30 years. Then answer "On Your Own" question 2.11.

Sulfer oxides ⟶

to reduce Sulfer Oxides
they do a Proces called cleening Coul to
reduce the Sulfer oxides imited by Coal
Also the Use Scrubbers to reduce
the Sulfer oxides imited By Smokstacks

Airborne lead ⟶

To elemanate Airborn Lead
U.S govement mandated that
Autombil manufacturers had to mak
Automobils run on Unleeded
gus

Carbon monoxide ⟶

in 1975 they made
Catalytic converters to
convert most of the
carbon monixices into
carbon dioxide.

ON YOUR OWN

2.11 Suppose you could institute regulations that would be targeted at one specific air pollutant. Based on the data in figure 2.9, which air pollutant would be best to target from a cost/benefit point of view?

Probobly Nitrogen oxides because the Pollustion Level is still extremly high.

Complete the study guide questions and have your parent correct them. If you need additional practice, you may wish to complete the optional summary for this module, located in the summary section of this notebook. Take time to understand anything that you may have missed and review your notes before taking the test for this module.

Study Guide

1 Write out the definitions for the following terms:

a. Humidity

The Moister Content of the Air

b. Absolute humidity

The mass of water vaper contained in a certain volome of Air

c. Relative humidity

The ratio of the mass of water vaper in the Air at a given temperature to the maxamine mass of water vapor the air could hold at that temperature exprissed as a percentage.

d. Greenhouse effect

regulates the temperature of the earth

e. Parts per million

The number of molecules (or Atoms) of a Substance in a mixture for every 1 million molecules (Atoms) in that Mixture

2 The temperature is the same at 1:00 p.m. on two consecutive days. For a person who is outside working, however, the second day feels cooler than the first day. On which day was the relative humidity higher? the first days relative humidity was higher

3 A child decides to keep his goldfish outside in a small bowl. He has to add water every day to keep the bowl full. On two consecutive days, the temperatures are very similar, but on the first day the relative humidity is 90%, while on the second day it is 60%. On which day will the child add more water to the goldfish bowl?

On the second day, because the relative humidity is lower 60% < 90%.

4 If you put a glass of water outside when the relative humidity is 100%, how quickly will the water evaporate? it will not evaporate at all.

5 Why does sweating cool people down?

because win you sweat, the Sun evaporates the heat in your sweat.

6 What is the percentage of nitrogen in dry air? What about oxygen?

nitrogen = 78%   oxygen = 21%.

7 What would be the consequence of removing all the carbon dioxide in the earth's air supply?

the earth would get Colder

8 What would be the consequence of removing all the ozone in the earth's air supply?

more ultra violet light would hit the earth and every living tissue would die

9 What would be the consequence of a sudden increase in the concentration of oxygen in the earth's air supply?

it would be unhealthy to humans and increase in natural fires

10 Suppose astronomers found another solar system in which there was a sun just like our sun. Suppose further that a planet in this new solar system was just as far from its sun as is Earth from our sun. Since the vast majority of energy that planets get comes from their suns, is it reasonable to assume that the new planet would have roughly the same average temperature as that of Earth? Why or why not?

it might if it hase the gases like in our Atmouspher it wouldnt if it didnt

11 What makes up the majority of the air we exhale?

Nitrogen

12 Do we exhale more carbon dioxide or more oxygen?

Oxygen

13 Do the data indicate any significant global warming?

in your mind no, but in real life YES

14 The current concentration of ground-level ozone in the air is about 0.110 ppm. What is that in percent?

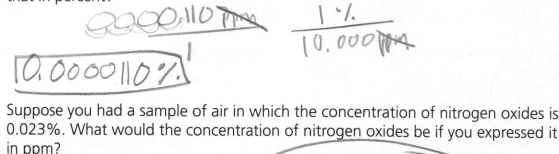

$$0.110 \text{ ppm} \qquad \frac{1\%}{10,000 \text{ ppm}}$$

$$\boxed{0.0000110\%.}$$

15 Suppose you had a sample of air in which the concentration of nitrogen oxides is 0.023%. What would the concentration of nitrogen oxides be if you expressed it in ppm?

$$\frac{0.023\%}{1} \qquad \frac{10,000 \text{ ppm}}{1\%} \qquad \boxed{230.0 \text{ PPMS}}$$

16 Is the air cleaner today, or was it cleaner 30 years ago?

today

17 What is a cost/benefit analysis?

It determins if the benefit is worth the cost

18 What does a catalytic converter do in a car?

Converts _most_ Carbon monoxide into Carbon dioxide

19 What does a scrubber do in a smokestack?

helps clean Sulfur oxides out of the Smokestak

20 In the United States, many regulations are aimed at decreasing the amount of ground-level ozone in the air because ground-level ozone is considered a pollutant. At the same time, many regulations are aimed at increasing the amount of ozone in the ozone layer. Despite the fact that ozone in the ozone layer is the same as ground-level ozone, ozone in the ozone layer is not considered a pollutant. Instead, it is considered an essential substance. Why?

because it blocks most of the ultraviolet light at of earth and because the ozone layer wiss above sea Level so we cant breath it in

MODULE 3

The Atmosphere

Introduction & Atmospheric Pressure—Part 1

Read pages 55–59 in the text. Complete experiment 3.1 and fill out the lab report. After you have completed the experiment, label the drawings below and explain how the experiment models what happens with a barometer. Remember to include your explanation in your lab report conclusion.

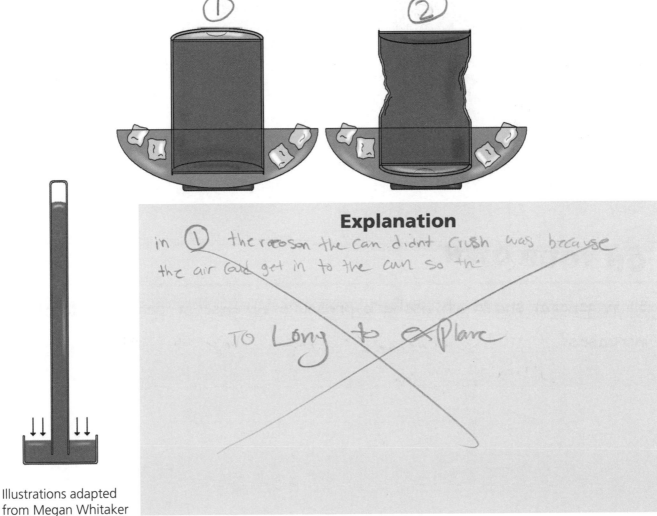

Explanation

in ① the reason the can didnt crush was because the air could get in to the can so the

TO Long to explane

Illustrations adapted
from Megan Whitaker

Atmospheric Pressure—Part 2 & The Layers of Earth's Atmosphere

Read pages 60–61 in the text. As you read, use the Venn diagram below to explain the difference between the homosphere and the heterosphere. Then answer "On Your Own" questions

Homosphere   **Heterosphere**

The part of the Atmospheric that is above 80 Kilometers aboc Sea-level

Part of the earth's atmosphere

isʃ higher, then roughly 80 Kilometers above Sea-level

ON YOUR OWN

3.1 In general, should atmospheric pressure increase or decrease as altitude increases? Probably decrease because there is Less Air upove you

ON YOUR OWN

3.2 The atmospheric pressure is 1.1 atm. Which of the following values for atmospheric pressure would you see in the weather report: 29.9 inches, 32.9 inches, or 28.1 inches? Well, for 1.0 atm the mercury level is 29.9 inches, so the atm is higher 1.1 so it is higher then 29.9 so it is 32.9 in

ON YOUR OWN

3.3 In chemistry, mixtures are classified as being either heterogeneous or homogeneous. Based on what you learned about the difference between the heterosphere and homosphere, classify milk as a heterogeneous or homogeneous mixture. What about Italian salad dressing?

milk homogeneous   Italian dressing heterogeneous

ON YOUR OWN

3.4 If an airplane travels at altitudes of over 4 kilometers, it is required to have a special oxygen supply for the pilot. As you learned, however, that altitude is well within the homosphere, where the air is 21% oxygen. Why, then, does the pilot need a special oxygen supply at this altitude? because the air is thinner, there is less Air higher up. but Oxygen is still 21% of the air mixture up there.

The Homosphere

Read pages 62–65 in the text. As you read, label the diagram below to help you remember the layers of the homosphere. Then answer "On Your Own" questions 3.5–3.6.

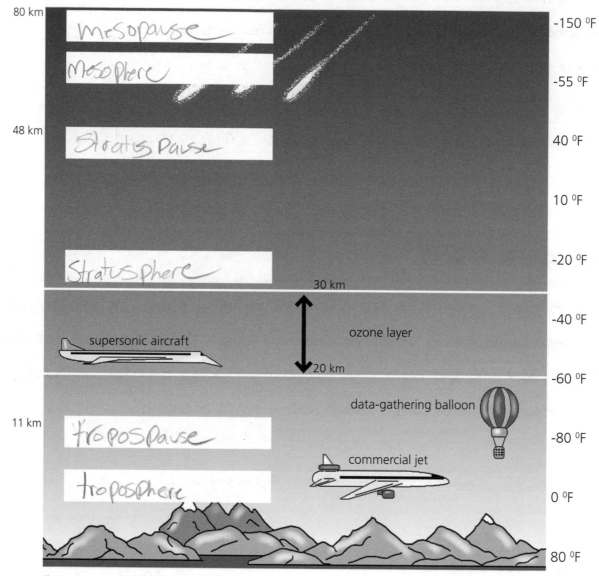

80 km	-150 °F
Mesopause	
Mesophere	-55 °F
48 km	
Stratopause	40 °F
	10 °F
	-20 °F
Stratusphere	
30 km	-40 °F
supersonic aircraft — ozone layer	
20 km	-60 °F
data-gathering balloon	
11 km	-80 °F
tropospause	
troposphere — commercial jet	0 °F
	80 °F

Illustration adapted from Megan Whitaker

ON YOUR OWN

3.5 A supersonic jet travels in the stratosphere. If such a plane were flying over a region experiencing thunderstorms, how would the supersonic jet be affected? *it probably would not be affected because most weather conditions happen in the troposphere and tropospause.*

ON YOUR OWN

3.6 Water freezes at 32 degrees Fahrenheit. Suppose you were able to watch a sealed vial of water travel up through the homosphere. It would freeze once it got 5 to 7 kilometers high. Would the frozen water ever melt as the vial traveled farther up? If so, where would this happen? it would happen in the Stratospause which is 40°F.

What Is Temperature?

Read pages 66–68 in the text. Complete experiment 3.2 and fill out the lab report. Then fill in the Venn diagram below to help you understand the new material. Make sure to explain how the two terms are related and how the two terms are different. Then answer "On Your Own" questions 3.7–3.8.

Heat

- energy that is transferred as a consequence of temperature change differances

Heat is just the tranfer of energy from one substance to another

Heat and temperature are linked because to have temperature you must have heat, and to have heat you must have temperature

Temperature

A measure of the energy of random motion in a substance's molecules

the measure of the average speed at which the molecules of a substance are moving

ON YOUR OWN

3.7 Two cold bricks are put in contact with one another. The first one has a temperature of -1.00 degrees celsius, and the other has a temperature of -10.00 degrees celsius. Is there any heat in this two-block system? Yes, because the energy from the -1.00 block tranferes to the -10.00 block because the TEMPURATURE of the -1.00°C is higher then the -10.00°C block

ON YOUR OWN

3.8 A thermometer reads 25.00 degrees celsius. Suppose you put that thermometer into a liquid, and the thermometer reading increases to 80.17 degrees celsius. A bright observer notes that the temperature of the substance was actually a tad higher than 80.17 degrees celsius the instant the thermometer was placed in it. Is the observer correct? why or why not? ~~I think the observer was correct because not all the energy will tranfere into the thermometer.~~ Yes because the instent the thermometer was placed in the substance, it took some energy from it reselting in its cooling, therefore the substance was slightly warmer before the theremometer was put in

The Temperature Gradient in the Homosphere &
The "Hole" in the Ozone Layer

Read pages 69–73 in the text. Then answer "On Your Own" questions 3.9–3.10.

ON YOUR OWN

3.9 Those who are against the CFC ban point out that CFCs are four to eight times heavier than the nitrogen and oxygen in the air. As a result, they say, there is no way that CFCs can float up to the ozone layer. Why are they wrong? because CFCs are harmless So nothing stops CFCs from floughting up Here

ON YOUR OWN

3.10 Those who are for the CFC ban claim that skin cancer rates have increased in Australia as a result of the "ozone hole." Although skin cancer rates have increased in Australia (and around the world), why is it hard to believe that the increase is a result of the ozone hole?

The ozone hole is Centered over Antartica and exists when the Polar vortex cones

41

The Heterosphere

Read pages 73–76 in the text. Use figure 3.8 to complete the drawing below. Answer "On Your Own" question 3.11. Then learn more about auroras by completing the "Digging Deeper" activity.

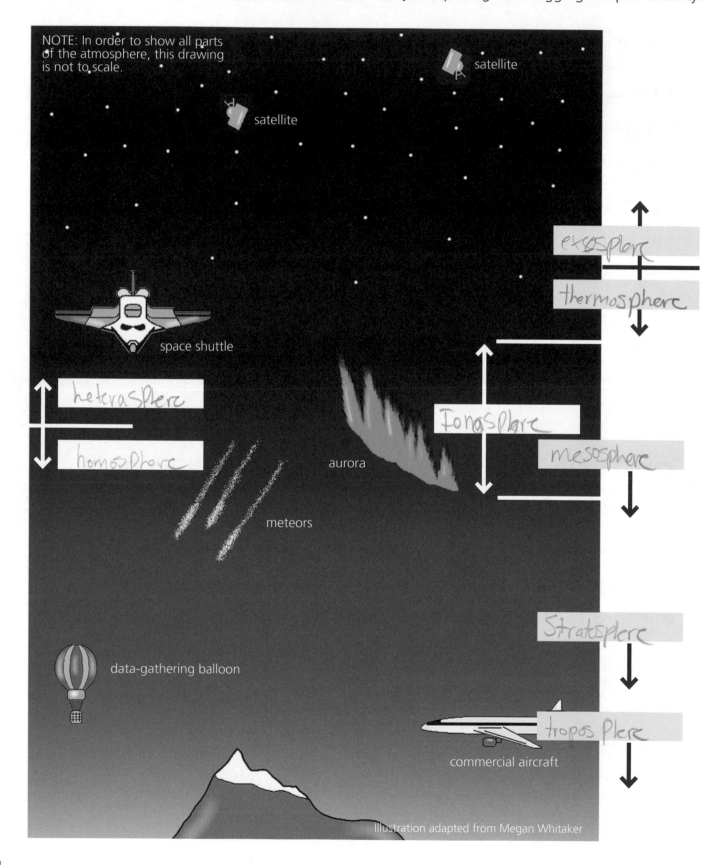

NOTE: In order to show all parts of the atmosphere, this drawing is not to scale.

satellite

satellite

exosphere

thermosphere

space shuttle

heterosphere

Ionosphere

homosphere

mesosphere

aurora

meteors

Stratosphere

data-gathering balloon

troposphere

commercial aircraft

Illustration adapted from Megan Whitaker

ON YOUR OWN

3.11 Sometimes, disturbances in the sun's magnetic field can cause disturbances in the ionosphere. Suppose you were listening to an AM radio at the time of such a disturbance. Would you notice? What if you were listening to a shortwave radio transmission from another continent? No disturbence in the AM radio, but a disturbence in the shortwave radio because they bounce their signals of of the Ionosphere

DIGGING DEEPER
Auroras

If you'd like to learn more about auroras and watch some very interesting footage of auroras, check out the websites below. Make sure to click on the video link in the first one.

link.apologia.com/ECPS2N/3.1
link.apologia.com/ECPS2N/3.2

Complete the study guide questions and have your parent correct them. If you need additional practice, you may wish to complete the optional summary for this module, located in the summary section of this notebook. Take time to understand anything that you may have missed and review your notes before taking the test for this module.

Study Guide

1 Write out the definitions for the following terms:

a. Atmosphere

The mass of Air Surrounding the planet

b. Atmospheric pressure

The pressure exerted by the Atmospher on all things in it

c. Barometer

an Instrument that measures Atmospheric pressure

d. Homosphere

the lower Layer of the earths Atmosphere,
is from ground Level to 80 kilometers above ground-Level

e. Heterosphere

the upper layer of the earths atmosphere.
exist from 80 kilometers = higher

f. Troposphere

the region in the earths atmo

The lowest region in the homosphere, exists from ground level to 11 klome

g. Stratosphere

The region of the earths atmosphere that
exists from 11 kilometers to 48 kilometers.

h. Mesosphere

the region which exists from roughly 48 kilometers to
80 kilometers

i. Jet streams

Narrow bands of high speed winds that circle the
earth, blowing from west to east.

j. Heat

is energy that is transfered as a Consequence of
temperature

k. Temperature

The measure of the energy of random motion in a substances
molecules (Atoms)

l. Thermosphere

the region of the Atmosphere that exists from
roughly 80 kilometers - 460 kilometers

m. Exosphere

the region of the earths Atmosphere that exist from roughly
460 kilometers beyond

n. Ionosphere

the region of the earths Atmosphere that exists
between roughly 65 and 330 kilometers, where gases are
Ionized

2 Suppose the earth's atmosphere contained twice the number of molecules it does today. Would atmospheric pressure be greater than, equal to, or less than it is now?

Probably will have greater Atmospheric Pressure then
todays

3 Two students make two different barometers. Although they are placed side by side so that they are both exposed to exactly the same atmospheric pressure, the column of liquid in the first student's barometer is significantly lower than the column of water in the second student's barometer. Assuming both students made their barometers correctly, what explains the difference?

it depense on Whhat liquid they put
in their barometers. if the liquid is pure water the barometer will
be taller, so the water will appear higher or lower compared to a
barometer with mercury.

4 The average, sea-level value for atmospheric pressure is 14.7 pounds per square inch, which is the same as 29.9 inches of mercury. If the atmospheric pressure is 0.85 atms, which of the following values would correspond to atmospheric pressure as reported in a weather report?

31.1 inches of mercury   29.9 inches of mercury   (25.4 inches of mercury)

$$\frac{0.85}{100} \cdot \frac{29.9}{10} = \frac{}{1000}$$

$$\frac{0.85 \text{ atm}}{1} \cdot \frac{29.9 \text{ in m}}{14.7 \text{ atm}}$$

$$\frac{25415}{1000} = 25.4 \text{ inches per mercury}$$

5 Two vials contain air samples taken at different altitudes. The first is composed of 21% oxygen, 78% nitrogen, and 1% other. The second is 95% helium, 4% hydrogen, and 1% other. Which came from the homosphere? *The on*

With 21% O, 78% n and 1% other

6 You are reading the data coming from a data-gathering balloon as it rises in the atmosphere. You have no idea what altitude it is at, but the balloon is sending a signal from its thermometer, telling you the temperature of its surroundings. How will you know when the balloon enters the stratosphere? How will you know when it enters the mesosphere? *You will know if it is entering the Stratosphere if the thermometer is at a higher temperature, when the temperature goes down, the balloon is entering the mesosphere*

7 Name the three regions of the homosphere, from lowest to highest.

troposphere, Stratosphere, mesosphere

8 Although the temperature gradient changes from region to region in the homosphere, there is one gradient that stays the same. It continues to decrease as you increase in altitude, no matter where you are in the homosphere. What gradient?

the Atmospheric pressure gradient?

9 A plane is experiencing a lot of problems because of a storm in the area. Is the plane flying in the troposphere or the stratosphere?

the troposphere

10 A scientist has two vials of ammonia gas. She tells you that in the first vial, the gas molecules are traveling with an average speed of 1,000 miles per hour. In the second vial, they are traveling with an average speed of 1,300 miles per hour. Which vial contains the gas with the higher temperature?

the one with the average speed of 1,300 mpH

11 As you are outside on a cold winter night, you begin to shiver from the cold. Your companion says that you are shivering from the heat. Is your companion correct? Why or why not? The Companion is Sorta right. I am Shivering from the loss of heat. the ~~transfer of energy in my bo~~ the energy my body would transffore to a different place, leving me colder

12 Suppose there were a layer of carbon dioxide gas in the mesosphere. What would happen to the temperature gradient in that region? it would get higher?

13 Why will the ban on CFCs most likely not save or improve people's lives?

14 Why will the ban on CFCs most likely result in a tragic loss of human life?

~~becu~~

15 Even though human civilization is responsible for less than 1% of all chlorine in the atmosphere, it is responsible for 80% of all ozone-destroying chlorine. Why?

16 What makes it possible for CFCs to travel up to the ozone layer and begin destroying ozone? the Polar vortex

17 Where is the ionosphere, and what makes it useful to us?

the Ionosphere is in the Upper Portion of the mesosphere and the lower Pootion of the thermosphere

it is usefull for short wave radios

The Wonder of Water

Introduction & The Composition of Water

Read pages 81–84 in the text. Complete experiment 4.1 and fill out the lab report. Then complete "On Your Own" question 4.1.

ON YOUR OWN

4.1 Suppose you want a precise measurement of rainfall in your area, so you set a rain gauge outside. After it rains, you measure the level of water in the gauge and record the result. You then empty the rain gauge and wait for the next rain. There are at least two sources of possible experimental error with this procedure. One will lead to a measurement that is too low, and the other will lead to a measurement that is too high. what are these sources of error?

Chemical Formulas

Read pages 85–86 in the text. Then complete "On Your Own" questions 4.2–4.4.

ON YOUR OWN

4.2 The chemical formula for baking soda is $NaHCO_3$. How many atoms make up one molecule of baking soda?

Six atoms

$Na=1 \quad H=1 \quad C=1 \quad O=3 \quad 1+1+1+3=6$

ON YOUR OWN

4.3 Vinegar's active ingredient is acetic (uh see' tik) acid, $C_2H_4O_2$. How many of each atom are present in a molecule of acetic acid? (See the discussion on page 85 in the text if you forget what the symbols mean.)

Carbon = 2   Hydrogen = 4   Oxygen = 2

ON YOUR OWN

4.4 The sugar in green, leafy vegetables is called glucose. A molecule of glucose contains 6 carbon atoms, 12 hydrogen atoms, and 6 oxygen atoms. what is the chemical formula of glucose?

$C_6H_{12}O_6$

Water's Polarity

Read pages 86–89 in the text. Complete experiment 4.2 and fill out the lab report. In your reading, you'll notice the author discusses chemical bonds in which atoms share electrons. These types of bonds are called **covalent** bonds. The prefix "co-" means "together," which is an easy way to remember that covalent chemical bonds result from the sharing of electrons. Covalent bonds are very strong and are one of the important types of chemical bonds you will learn more about in biology and chemistry. Use figures 4.2 and 4.3 to identify the parts of a water molecule below. Make sure to identify the type of bond shown and the partial polarity. Then complete "On Your Own" questions 4.5–4.7.

Oxygen Atom

Covalent bond

Covalent bond

hydrogen Atom

Hedygen Atom

ON YOUR OWN

4.5 Suppose you had a positively charged object to hold next to the stream of water in experiment 4.2. Would the stream bend the same way as it did with the comb, or would it bend the opposite way? Why?

It will bend the same way because the Negativly charged parts of the water molecule will be attracted to the positively charged object

ON YOUR OWN

4.6 Hydrochloric acid, HCl, is a powerful acid often used in cleaning. While "H" stands for hydrogen, "Cl" stands for chlorine. Chlorine atoms can pull on electrons much more strongly than can hydrogen atoms. Is HCl polar? If so, where is the small negative charge: on the chlorine atom or the hydrogen atom?

Hydrochloric acid is polar. The chlorine atoms are the ones with the small negative charge

ON YOUR OWN

4.7 Chlorine gas, Cl₂, is a molecule composed of two chlorine atoms bonded together with a chemical bond. Is this molecule polar? Why or why not?

It is not polar because the chlorine atoms pull the electrons with equal force.

Water as a Solvent

Read pages 90–93 in the text. Complete experiment 4.3 and fill out the lab report. Read carefully the section about how ionic compounds are formed. When salt, an ionic compound, is formed, the sodium atom loses an electron to the chlorine atom. When this transfer of electrons occurs to form ionic compounds (the positively charged sodium ion is attracted to the negatively charged chlorine ion), the attraction bond between the oppositely charged ions is called an ionic bond. Ionic bonds are another one of the important types of chemical bonds you will learn more about in biology and chemistry. Remember, scientists classify in order to help make sense of things, and chemical bonds are no exception.

Complete the "Digging Deeper" exercise. Explain in your own words how water can dissolve polar molecules, ionic compounds, and nonpolar molecules. Then complete "On Your Own" questions 4.8–4.9.

DIGGING DEEPER
Formation of Water Shells Around Ions

To see a 2-D animation of how water dissolves ions, check out the website below. Make sure to click on the activity to download it. You will need to change the charge of the purple and green ions to see how water dissolves them. Try it a couple of times!

link.apologia.com/ECPS2N/4.1

How does water dissolve polar and ionic molecules?

_____

_____

_____

_____

_____

_____

ON YOUR OWN

4.8 Water does not dissolve gasoline. Is gasoline most likely made up of ionic, polar, or nonpolar molecules?

nonpolar molecules

ON YOUR OWN

4.9 Suppose you did experiment 4.3 with gasoline instead of water. (Don't actually do it; the fumes are dangerous!) Would table salt dissolve in gasoline? What about canola oil? *gasoline is nonpolar,*
Salt is an Ionic compound so gasline will not dissolve
salt, it will dissolve canola oil though because canola oil is
nonpolar

Hydrogen Bonding in Water

Read pages 93–96 in the text. Complete experiment 4.4 and fill out the lab report. To help you remember the differences between liquid and solid water, list several of them in the Venn diagram below as you read this section. Then complete "On Your Own" questions 4.10–4.11.

Liquid Water　　　　　　　　　　　　　　　**Solid Water**

ON YOUR OWN

4.10 Water has a very high boiling point (the temperature at which it boils) compared to most other substances that are liquid at room temperature. Use hydrogen bonding to explain why this is the case.

because Hydrogen bonds hold water molecules together, It takes a lot of Heat (energy) to pull them apart

ON YOUR OWN

4.11 Butane is a gas at room temperature, but it is stored under pressure as a liquid in a butane lighter. The chemical formula is C_4H_{10}. Isopropyl alcohol (commonly called rubbing alcohol) is another liquid you might have around the house. Its chemical formula is C_3H_8O. One of these liquids participates in hydrogen bonding. Which one?

C_3H_8O does or Isopropyl alcohol because it has Hydrogen.

Water's Cohesion—Part 1

Read pages 97–99 in the text. Complete experiment 4.5 and fill out the lab report. Complete the graphic organizer below to reinforce how the hydrogen bonding of water allows for the property of cohesion, which is very important for living things. Start by writing out what hydrogen bonding is, then complete the rest of the organizer.

Hydrogen Bonding

Hydrogen bonding bonds Hydrogen Atom from one molecule to the Oxygen Atom of another molecule. Sharing Electrons

↓

Cohesion

The Phenomenon that occurs when individual molecules are so strongly attracted to each other that they tend to stay together, even when exposed to tension

Surface Tension

is caused by cohesion, Because of cohesion, liquids and resist tension

Cohesion-Tension Transport

Water's Cohesion—Part 2 & Hard Water and Soft Water

Read pages 99–101 in the text. Complete experiment 4.6 and fill out the lab report. Then find out what God's Word says and complete "On Your Own" question 4.12.

WHAT DOES GOD'S WORD SAY?

God's word has a lot to say about water! Just like there would be no life without water, there is no eternal life without Jesus. Look up the following scriptures and write them down. Then explain how Jesus is our spiritual water.

Isaiah 55:1

John 4:14

ON YOUR OWN

4.12 Calcium and magnesium ions are both the result of atoms that lose electrons. Thus, they are positively charged ions. Suppose you actually could remove calcium and magnesium ions from water without replacing them with other positive ions. If you slowly started removing only calcium and magnesium ions from the water, you would find that as time went on, removal of the ions would become more and more difficult. Eventually, it would be nearly impossible to remove any more calcium or magnesium ions in the water, even though there might still be many ions left. Why? As time went on, the water itself would become more and more negatively charged. Negative charges attract positive charges. Thus, with each positive Ion you remove, the tap water would become more negative, and that would more strongly attract the remaining positive Ions. At some point the negative charge of the tap water would be so great that it would attract the remaining positive Ions so strongly that it would take enormous amounts of energy to pull the positive Ions away.

Complete the study guide questions and have your parent correct them. If you need additional practice, you may wish to complete the optional summary for this module, located in the summary section of this notebook. Take time to understand anything that you may have missed and review your notes before taking the test for this module.

Study Guide

1 Write out the definitions for the following terms:

a. Electrolysis

The use of electricity to brake up molecules into (Atoms)

b. Polar molecule

a molecule that has both negative and positive charge due to the imbalence in the way electrons are shared

c. Solvent

The liquid substance capable of dissolving other substances

d. Solute

A substance that can be dissolved by solvents

e. Cohesion

f. Hard water

Water that has certain dissolved Ions in it— predominatly calcium and magnesium

2 Suppose you did an electrolysis experiment like experiment 4.1 on hydrogen peroxide, which has a chemical formula of H_2O_2. If it worked properly, which of the following results would you expect? (Check the appropriate box.)

☐ a. same as with water

☑ b. equal amounts of hydrogen and oxygen

☐ c. twice as much oxygen as hydrogen

3 Suppose you performed experiment 4.1 with a test tube that had a crack in it. Gas could slowly leak out that crack, but not nearly as quickly as it was being made in the experiment. Suppose further that the crack was in the test tube that held hydrogen gas. Which chemical formula might result from such a botched experiment: ⟨HO⟩ or H_4O?

4 Epsom salts, which you used in experiment 4.1, has the chemical formula $MgSO_4$. If Mg is the symbol for magnesium, S stands for sulfur, and O represents oxygen, how many of each atom exists in a molecule of Epsom salts?

5 Calcium carbonate is an ionic substance commonly called "chalk." If this molecule has one calcium atom (Ca), one carbon atom (C), and three oxygen atoms (O), what is its chemical formula?

6 One of the most common household cleaners is ammonia, which has a chemical formula of NH_3. How many atoms are in a molecule of ammonia?

7 A certain molecule is composed of atoms that all pull on electrons with the same strength. Will this molecule be polar?

8 Baking soda dissolves in water. Will it dissolve in vegetable oil, which is a nonpolar substance?

9 Carbon tetrachloride will not dissolve in water. Is it most likely made of ionic molecules, polar molecules, or nonpolar molecules?

10 Suppose you were able to count the molecules in a substance. Which would have more molecules, 1 liter of liquid water or 1 liter of ice?

11 If the substance in question 10 were virtually any other substance, what would the answer be?

What is responsible for water being a liquid at room temperature as well as for water's cohesion?

 What causes surface tension?

 Why is water harder in certain regions of the world than in others?

The Hydrosphere

Introduction &
The Parts of the Hydrosphere and the Hydrologic Cycle—Part 1

Read pages 105–109 in the text. Complete the following concept map to help you remember the new information you will learn as you read about the hydrologic cycle.

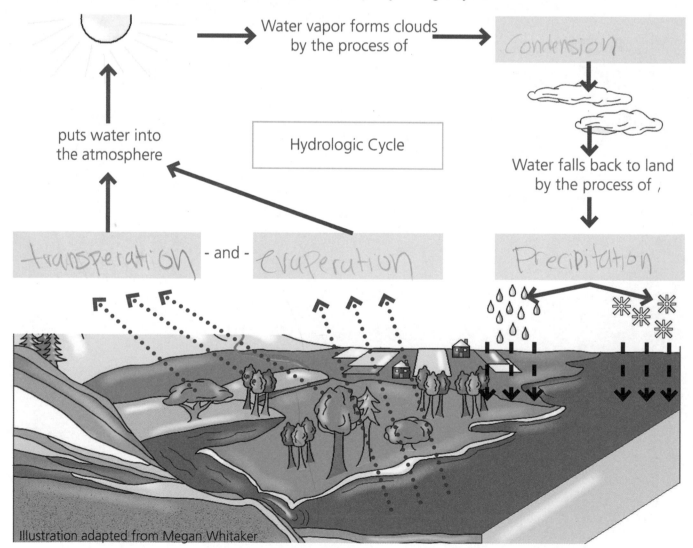

Water vapor forms clouds by the process of → Condension

puts water into the atmosphere

Hydrologic Cycle

Water falls back to land by the process of

transperation - and - evaperation

Precipitation

Illustration adapted from Megan Whitaker

The Parts of the Hydrosphere and the Hydrologic Cycle—Part 2

Read pages 109–113 in the text. Complete experiment 5.1 and fill out the lab report. Then answer "On Your Own" questions 5.1–5.4.

ON YOUR OWN

5.1 Suppose you are given a sample of water taken from somewhere in the earth's hydrosphere.

a. Would it most likely be saltwater or freshwater?

freshwater

b. If it is freshwater, where did it most likely come from?

the ocean

c. If the person who collected the sample tells you it is freshwater that originally came from a liquid source, where did it most likely come from?

Iceburgs or glaciers

ON YOUR OWN

5.2 Water that was originally in a plant ends up in a cloud. What two processes of the hydrologic cycle caused it to be transferred in that way?

trasperation condition

ON YOUR OWN

5.3 Rain that hits the land can travel as a liquid into a lake, river, stream, or ocean in two different ways. what are they?

Surface run off or groundwater flow

ON YOUR OWN

5.4 Suppose a scientist studies two groundwater sources. The first is an underground river that flows quickly into a large lake. The second is a large basin of underground water that moves at a much slower rate toward a small pond. which groundwater source has the longest residence time?

The large busion of underground water that moves at a much slower rate toward a small pond

The Ocean

Read pages 113–116 in the text. Discover more about oceans and the hydrologic cycle by completing the "Digging Deeper" activity. Then answer "On Your Own" questions 5.5–5.6.

DIGGING DEEPER
Oceans

To learn more about how much water the oceans hold and other interesting facts about oceans and the hydrologic cycle, check out these websites:

link.apologia.com/ECPS2N/5.1

link.apologia.com/ECPS2N/5.2

Write out two facts that you didn't know before in the space below.

Write what you think of this Book.

Well, The person who wrote the Learning Book is sharing his or her opinions, This IS A SCIENCE BOOK! The writer is suppose to teach not force his opinions on me! why oh why oh why, He IS Denying EVALUTION!!

ON YOUR OWN

5.5 Suppose you analyzed the salinity of three samples of ocean water. One was taken from deep in the ocean, one was taken from near the surface, and one was taken from a place near where a large river emptied into the ocean. If the salinities of samples 1, 2, and 3 were 37 grams per kilogram, 25 grams per kilogram, and 35 grams per kilogram, respectively, which sample was taken near the river?

25 grams Per Kilogram

ON YOUR OWN

5.6 If a lake were completely isolated from all rivers and streams so that the only way it could get rid of water was by evaporation, would it most likely be a freshwater or saltwater source?

It would most likly be Satwater.

Glaciers and Icebergs

Read pages 116–120 in the text. Complete experiment 5.2 and fill out the lab report. Complete the graphic organizer below with facts about the different terms you will read about in this section. Then answer "On Your Own" question 5.7.

Push

Calving

ON YOUR OWN

5.7 A sailor brings you a chunk of ice that he thinks came from an iceberg. Based on the description of what he saw, however, you think that it might have been a large chunk of sea ice. How could you tell whether the ice is from an iceberg or from sea ice?

Groundwater and Soil Moisture & Surface Water

Read pages 120–122 in the text. Write a paragraph explaining what happens to a drop of rainwater as it travels from the sky until it becomes a part of our groundwater. Include the following terms: soil moisture, percolation, water table, saturated. Then answer "On Your Own" questions 5.8–5.9.

The Travels of a Raindrop

ON YOUR OWN

5.8 You are studying a sample of soil and want to know if it came from above or below the water table. What could you do to determine this?

ON YOUR OWN

5.9 In a certain region, the depth of the water table is measured. If there is a lot less rain than usual over the summer, what will happen to the depth of the water table?

Atmospheric Moisture

Read pages 122–126 in the text. Complete experiment 5.3 and fill out the lab report. Then answer "On Your Own" question 5.10.on.

ON YOUR OWN

5.10 Suppose you have a balloon whose volume you can change. You inflate it to a volume of 1 liter and measure the temperature of the gas inside. You then very quickly compress the balloon so that its volume is only 0.5 liters. What happens to the temperature of the gas inside?

Water Pollution

Read pages 126–127 in the text. Complete the "Digging Deeper" section to learn more about groundwater pollution.

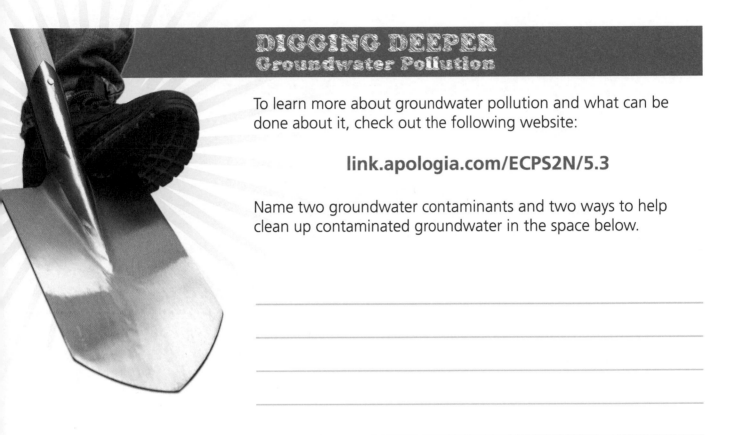

DIGGING DEEPER
Groundwater Pollution

To learn more about groundwater pollution and what can be done about it, check out the following website:

link.apologia.com/ECPS2N/5.3

Name two groundwater contaminants and two ways to help clean up contaminated groundwater in the space below.

Complete the study guide questions and have your parent correct them. If you need additional practice, you may wish to complete the optional summary for this module, located in the summary section of this notebook. Take time to understand anything that you may have missed and review your notes before taking the test for this module.

Study Guide

Write out the definitions for the following terms:

    a. Hydrosphere

    b. Hydrologic cycle

    c. Transpiration

    d. Condensation

    e. Precipitation

    f. Distillation

    g. Residence time

    h. Salinity

    i. Firn

    j. Water table

    k. Percolation

l. Adiabatic cooling

m. Cloud condensation nuclei

2 What kind of water makes up the majority of Earth's water supply?

3 What is the largest source of freshwater on the planet?

4 What is the largest source of *liquid* freshwater on the planet?

5 In the hydrologic cycle, name the ways water can enter the atmosphere.

6 When a raindrop hits the ground, name three ways it can eventually end up in a river.

7 What process in the hydrologic cycle puts soil moisture into the atmosphere?

8 In which body of water would the residence time be shorter: a quickly moving river or a lake that has no river outlets?

9 What must a lake have in order for it to be a freshwater lake?

 10 Why is the salinity of the ocean evidence that the earth is not billions of years old?

 11 If you tasted melted sea ice, would it taste like freshwater or saltwater?

 12 Where do icebergs come from?

 **13** Where do glaciers come from?

 14 What is the term for the process by which a portion of a glacier breaks off and falls into the water?

15 The captain of a ship sees an iceberg and steers clear of it. Why is the captain still worried about a collision?

16 Suppose you studied two areas of land close to one another. In the first, there are a lot of trees. In the second, there are almost no trees at all. Other than that, the two areas seem identical. They have the same kind of grass and experience the same weather. Which one has the deeper water table? Explain.

17 If no energy is added to air, what happens to the temperature when the air expands?

18 Will fog be thicker in a smoky area or an area free of smoke?

19 What kind of cooling is responsible for most cloud formation?

20 A bright student notes that with a few modifications, a refrigerator can become a "hot box," keeping things warm instead of cold. Explain.

21 What kind of water pollution is the hardest to track back to its source?

Earth and the Lithosphere

Introduction & The Crust

Read pages 131–133 in the text. Use the graphic organizer below to note the similarities and differences in the types of rock that make up the earth's crust. Then answer "On Your Own" question 6.1.

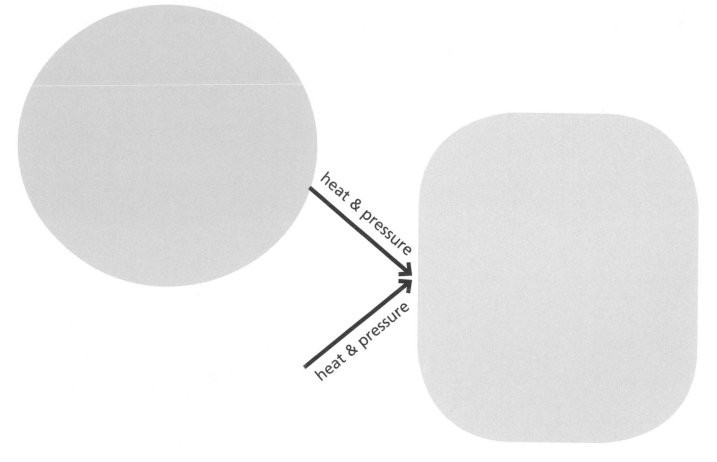

heat & pressure

heat & pressure

ON YOUR OWN

6.1 Consider the three types of rock mentioned in this section. Which one would be more likely to be found deep in the crust?

The Mantle—Part 1

Read pages 133–136 in the text. As you read, use the diagram below to identify the parts of the

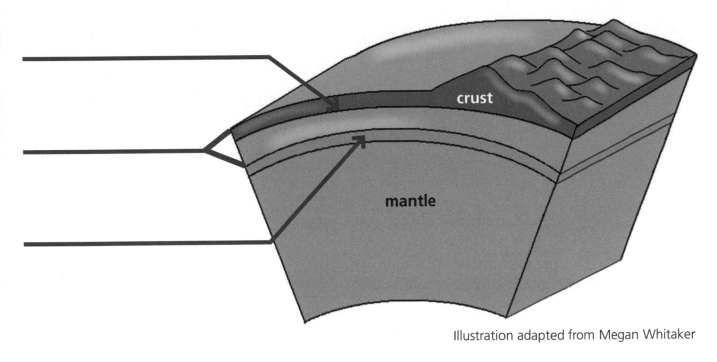

crust

mantle

Illustration adapted from Megan Whitaker

The Mantle—Part 2

Read pages 136–137 in the text. Complete experiment 6.2 and fill out the lab report. Then answer "On Your Own" questions 6.2–6.3.

ON YOUR OWN

6.2 Suppose you had a long steel rod and you stood at one end of it while a friend stood at the other end. Consider the following experiment: Your friend hits his end of the rod with a hammer, and you listen for the sound. You then press an ear against the rod, and your friend hits it with the hammer again. In which case would the sound be louder? NOTE: Please don't try this at home!

ON YOUR OWN

6.3 Suppose you were able to remove a sample of the plastic rock from the asthenosphere and take it into a laboratory. Would it behave differently than a rock sample you took from Earth's crust? Why or why not?

The Earth's Core

Read pages 138–144 in the text. Identify the two discontinuities you read about on the diagram below. Complete experiment 6.3 and fill out the lab report. Then answer "On Your Own" questions 6.4–6.5.

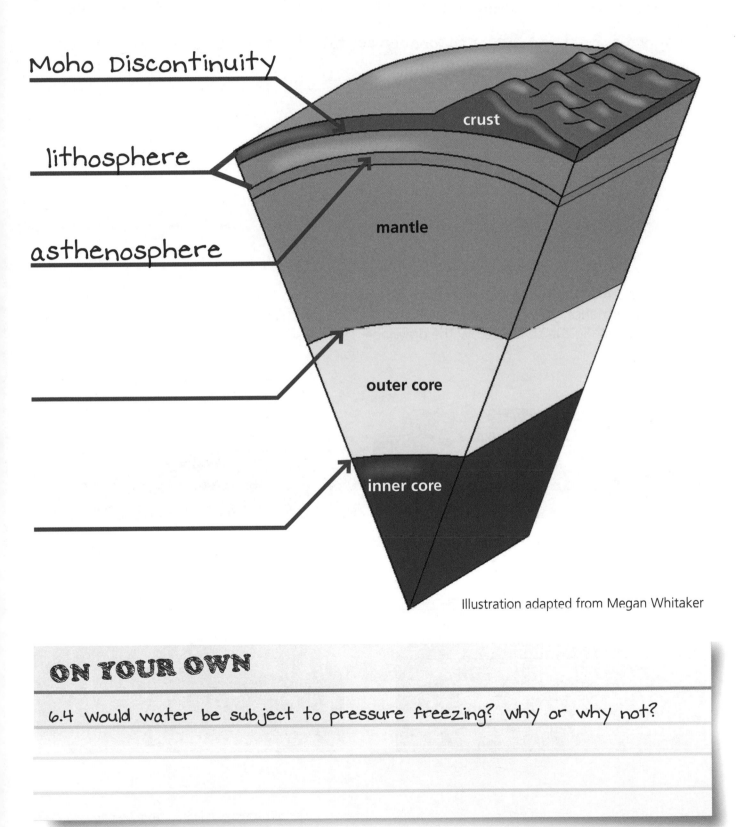

Moho Discontinuity

lithosphere

asthenosphere

crust

mantle

outer core

inner core

Illustration adapted from Megan Whitaker

ON YOUR OWN

6.4 Would water be subject to pressure freezing? Why or why not?

ON YOUR OWN

6.5 Regardless of whether the dynamo theory, the rapid-decay theory, or some as-yet-unknown theory is correct in explaining the earth's magnetic field, we are reasonably certain that substances in the core of the earth are in motion. Why?

Plate Tectonics

Read pages 144–148 in the text. Complete experiment 6.4 and fill out the lab report. To reinforce the new information you'll read about, identify the different plate interactions and give an example of each in the space below the drawings. Then answer "On Your Own" questions 6.6–6.7.

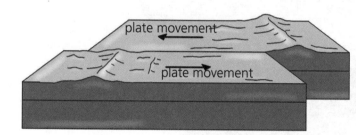

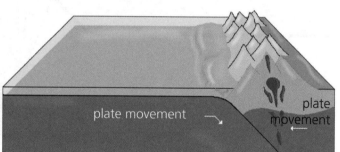

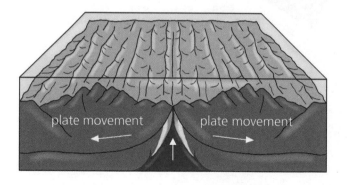

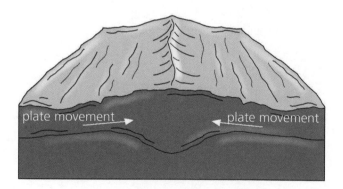

Illustrations adapted from Megan Whitaker

ON YOUR OWN

6.6 Would plate tectonics work if the mantle were made out of normal, solid rock?

ON YOUR OWN

6.7 Look at figure 6.3. Assuming plate tectonics is true, where would you expect the majority of the earthquakes in the United States to occur?

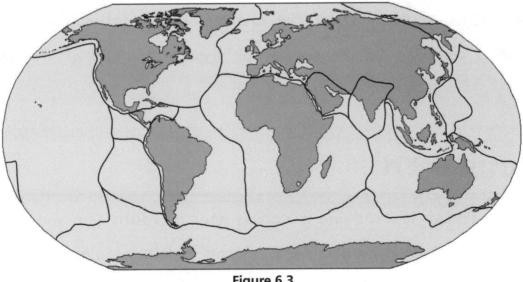

Figure 6.3
The Major Plates in the Lithosphere
Illustration by Megan Whitaker

Earthquakes

Read pages 148–151 in the text. Complete the following "Digging Deeper" activity. Then answer "On Your Own" questions 6.8–6.9.

DIGGING DEEPER
Earthquakes

Find out more about earthquakes at the USGS site:

link.apologia.com/ECPS2N/6.1

Then check out more interesting facts at this website:

link.apologia.com/ECPS2N/6.2

Use the space below to write two interesting things about earthquakes that you didn't know before visiting these sites.

_____

_____

_____

_____

_____

ON YOUR OWN

6.8 Suppose you could measure the energy of an earthquake at its focus. How would it compare to the energy of the earthquake at its epicenter?

ON YOUR OWN

6.9 A seismologist is studying a region near a fault. She measures two earthquakes. One measures 2 on the Richter scale, and the next measures 5. How many times more energy does the second earthquake release as compared to the first?

Mountains and Volcanoes

Read pages 151–153 in the text. Identify the types of mountains and give an example of each in the space below each drawing. Then answer "On Your Own" question 6.10.

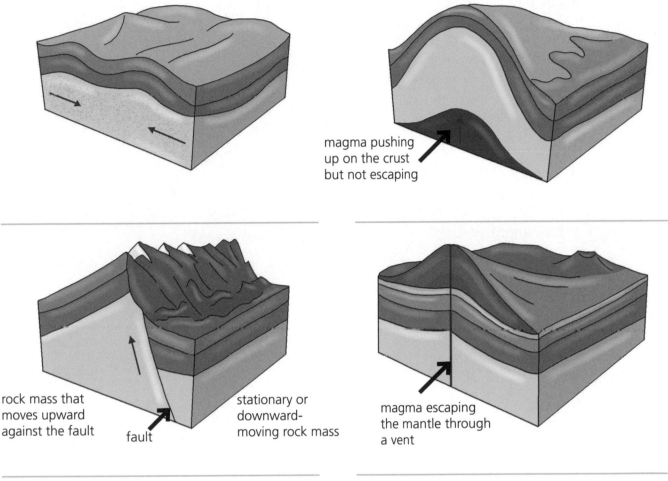

magma pushing up on the crust but not escaping

rock mass that moves upward against the fault

fault

stationary or downward-moving rock mass

magma escaping the mantle through a vent

Illustrations adapted from Megan Whitaker

ON YOUR OWN

6.10 Which kinds of mountains are formed as the result of rock masses moving against each other?

Complete the study guide questions and have your parent correct them. If you need additional practice, you may wish to complete the optional summary for this module, located in the summary section of this notebook. Take time to understand anything that you may have missed and review your notes before taking the test for this module.

Study Guide

1 Write out the definitions for the following terms:

    a. Earth's crust

    b. Sediment

    c. Sedimentary rock

    d. Igneous rock

    e. Metamorphic rock

    f. Plastic rock

    g. Earthquake

    h. Fault

    i. Focus

    j. Epicenter

2 Scientists often separate the earth into five distinct sections. Name those sections.

3 Of the five sections listed in question 2, which can we observe directly?

4 What two regions of the earth does the Moho discontinuity separate? What about the Gutenberg discontinuity? What about the Lehmann discontinuity?

5 What is the difference between the ways that igneous rock and sedimentary rock form?

6 Of the three types of rock discussed in this module, which type starts out as a different type of rock?

7 What is unique about the rock in the asthenosphere?

8 What is the main thing scientists observe in order to learn about the makeup of the earth's interior?

9 Which is solid: the inner core or the outer core? Why is it solid when the other is liquid?

10 Where is the magnetic field of the earth generated?

11 What causes the magnetic field of the earth?

12 Give a brief description of the two main theories that attempt to explain the earth's magnetic field.

 13 What makes the rapid-decay theory more scientifically valid than the dynamo theory?

14 Why is a catastrophe like the worldwide Flood in Noah's time an essential part of the earth's history if the rapid-decay theory is true?

 15 What two reasons make otherwise good scientists ignore the more scientifically valid rapid-decay theory?

16 Why would life cease to exist without the earth's magnetic field?

17 What are the "plates" in plate tectonics?

18 What can happen when plates collide with one another?

19 What is Pangaea?

20 Why do otherwise good scientists ignore the plate tectonics theory despite the evidence that exists for it?

21 What causes earthquakes?

22 Briefly describe the elastic rebound theory of earthquakes.

 23 A seismologist detects an earthquake that measures 4 on the Richter scale. Later, he detects one that measures 8. How many times more energy does the second earthquake release as compared to the first?

 24 Name the four kinds of mountains. What is required for the formation of each?

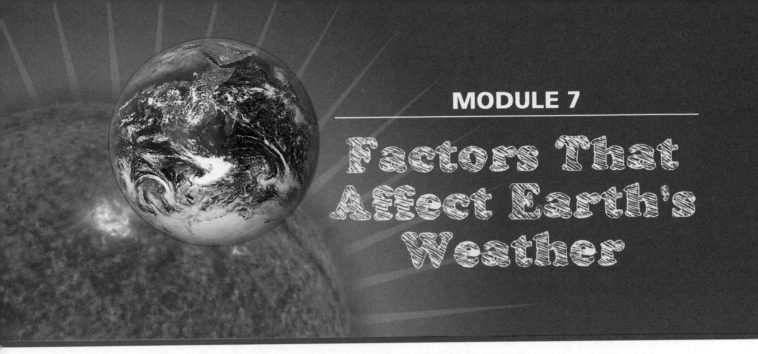

MODULE 7

Factors That Affect Earth's Weather

Introduction, Factors That Influence Weather & Clouds

Read pages 157–160 in the text. Use the diagram below to identify the different types of clouds you will read about in this section. Then answer "On Your Own" questions 7.1 – 7.2.

Illustration adapted from Megan Whitaker

ON YOUR OWN

7.1 Is it possible to have altocirrus clouds? Why or why not?

ON YOUR OWN

7.2 If a group of cumulus clouds were higher than typical cumulus clouds but were also dark, what would they be called?

Experiment 7.1 & Earth's Thermal Energy

Read over experiment 7.1 on pages 160–161 and start the experiment using the lab report in the back of this notebook. You will not complete this experiment until the end of module 8, so you will need to add to your data table daily. Next read pages 161–165 in the text. Use the organizer below to keep track of the new vocabulary you'll read about. Then answer "On Your Own" questions 7.3–7.5.

SCIENCE VOCABULARY	DEFINITION
Aphelion	
Perihelion	
Summer solstice	
Winter solstice	
Spring equinox	
Fall equinox	

ON YOUR OWN

7.3 Suppose the earth were tilted opposite of the way it is now. Would the Northern Hemisphere experience summer at the earth's aphelion or perihelion?

ON YOUR OWN

7.4 Between what dates is the length of the day less than 12 hours in the Southern Hemisphere and at the same time decreasing from day to day?

ON YOUR OWN

7.5 Suppose the earth's orbit around the sun were circular rather than elliptical. If that were true, the earth would always be the same distance from the sun. Under these conditions, would there still be seasons?

Latitude and Longitude &
Uneven Thermal Energy Distribution—Part 1

Remember to add to your data table for experiment 7.1. Read pages 165–169 in the text. To help you better understand the Coriolis effect that you'll read about on page 169, complete the following activity. You will need a friend to help you. Then complete the "Digging Deeper" section.

Coriolis Effect Demonstration

You will need a piece of cardboard or posterboard cut into a 10-inch circle, a pencil with an eraser, and two different colored pencils. Cut a hole in the center of the circle large enough for a pencil with an eraser to go through it. Now place the circle with the pencil through it on a table (eraser on the table so that the circle freely spins around the pencil). The eraser will be the North Pole.

Now have your friend hold the circle still while you draw a straight line from the North Pole (the eraser) to the equator (the edge of the circle) with one of the colored pencils. This will represent wind direction that is not affected by Earth's rotation. Next, using the other colored pencil, place it at the same spot that you started the first line, but have your friend rotate the circle counterclockwise as you draw straight line. Describe the difference between your lines in the space below.

_____

_____

_____

_____

_____

_____

_____

_____

_____

_____

DIGGING DEEPER
Winds

To find out more about wind and how it affects the weather, check out the website below:

link.apologia.com/ECPS2N/7.1

There are several activities you can do if you scroll down to the bottom of the page.

Uneven Thermal Energy Distribution—Part 2

Remember to add to your data table for experiment 7.1. To make sure that you understand what you read yesterday, review pages 166–169. Then read pages 170–171. Following the directions below, draw the global winds on the globe on the next page. Finally, answer "On Your Own" questions 7.6–7.8.

Global wind directions: Use a green pencil to draw the trade winds, an orange pencil to draw the prevailing westerlies, and a purple pencil to draw the polar easterlies. Remember to account for the Coriolis effect.

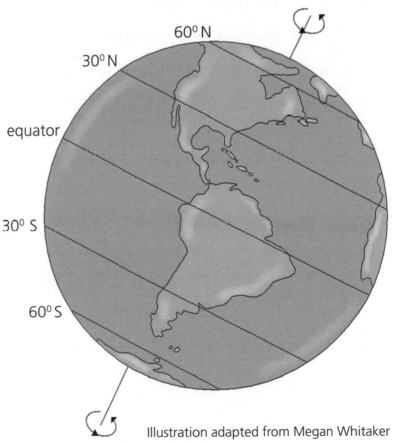

Illustration adapted from Megan Whitaker

ON YOUR OWN

7.6 On a day at the beach, you notice that the sand is so hot that it is hard to walk on it with bare feet. At the same time, however, the ocean is quite cool. When you left your hotel, you noticed no breeze at all, but when you got to the beach, you noticed a reasonably strong breeze. Is the wind blowing from the ocean to the shore or vice versa?

ON YOUR OWN

7.7 Suppose you want to fire a missile from southern California to a point in northern Canada that is due north of your location in California. Ignoring the effects of wind and weather, would you aim the missile due north, northwest, or northeast?

ON YOUR OWN

7.8 The global patterns of wind circulation in figure 7.9 indicate that in Mexico the winds should be blowing basically east to west. Does this mean that in Mexico the wind will never blow from west to east?

Air Masses

Read page 172–176 in the text. Use the graphic organizer below to explain the differences among the fronts you will read about in this section. Then answer "On Your Own" questions 7.9–7.10.

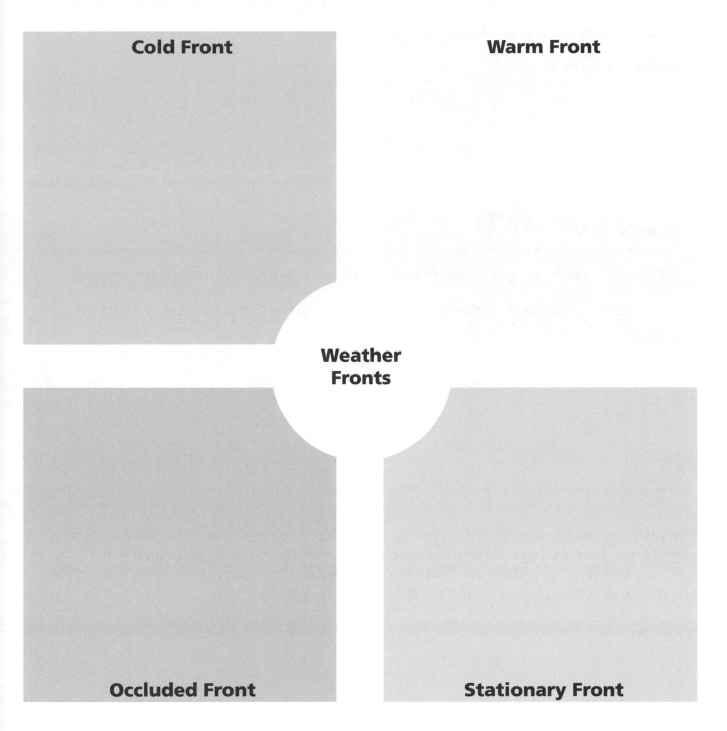

Cold Front

Warm Front

Weather Fronts

Occluded Front

Stationary Front

ON YOUR OWN

7.9 Suppose you were to observe a long, light rain. After the rain is over and the sky is clear, would you expect warmer temperatures or colder temperatures?

ON YOUR OWN

7.10 Why can't an occluded front start out with the weather typical of a cold front and then end with the weather typical of a warm front?

Complete the study guide questions and have your parent correct them. If you need additional practice, you may wish to complete the optional summary for this module, located in the summary section of this notebook. Take time to understand anything that you may have missed and review your notes before taking the test for this module

Study Guide

1 Write out the definitions for the following terms:

    a. Aphelion

    b. Perihelion

    c. Lines of longitude

    d. Lines of latitude

    e. Coriolis effect

    f. Air mass

    g. Weather front

2 What is the difference between weather and climate?

3 What are the three main factors that affect the earth's weather?

4 Be sure that you can identify each of the cloud types in figure 7.1.

5 If stratus clouds are dark, what are they called?

6 If you find lenticular clouds higher than normal, what are they called?

 7 What does "insolation" stand for?

 8 In the Northern Hemisphere, is the length of the days greater than or less than 12 hours between June 21 and September 22? Are the day lengths increasing or decreasing during that time?

 9 In the Southern Hemisphere, between what dates are the day lengths less than 12 hours but increasing?

 10 Is the Northern Hemisphere's summer during aphelion or perihelion?

 11 What causes wind?

 12 Why isn't there a constant stream of wind blowing from the poles to the equator?

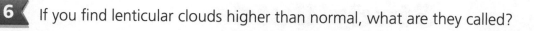 **13** What causes the wind patterns to bend in different regions of the globe?

14 Suppose you are in Alaska and would like to fire a missile to hit a target at the equator, due south of your location. Ignoring the effects of wind and air resistance, in which direction should you aim the missile?

15 At nighttime, high elevations usually cool faster than low elevations. Thus, at night, the land on a mountain is usually cooler than the land in the valley next to the mountain. Will the local wind produced by this effect blow from the mountain into the valley or from the valley up to the mountain?

16 Is the humidity high or low in a continental polar air mass? Is this air mass warm or cold?

17 Is the humidity high or low in a maritime tropical air mass? Is this air mass warm or cold?

18 Over a period of a couple of days, the clouds slowly build, and then a gentle, long rain ensues that lasts about 20 hours. What kind of front causes this weather?

19 Over a period of a few days, you notice cirrus clouds forming, followed by stratus and nimbostratus clouds. In just a few hours, however, dark cumulonimbus clouds form, heralding a thunderstorm. What kind of front caused this?

20 In less than a day, dark cumulonimbus clouds form and unleash a thunderstorm that lasts only a few hours. After the thunderstorm is over and the sky clears, do you expect cooler or warmer temperatures as compared to the temperature before the clouds began forming?

Weather and Its Prediction

Introduction & Precipitation

Remember to add data to your table for experiment 7.1. Read pages 181–183 in the text. Use the graphic organizer below to help you keep track of the different types of precipitation, as well as the two theories you will read about in this section. Then answer "On Your Own" questions 8.1–8.2.

	DESCRIPTION
Bergeron process	
Collision-coalescence process	
Rain	
Sleet	
Snow	
Drizzle	
Hail	
Dew	
Frost	

ON YOUR OWN

8.1 If a thunderstorm is not accompanied by strong, upward gusts of wind, will the thunderstorm produce hail?

ON YOUR OWN

8.2 How can you tell the difference between sleet and freezing rain?

Thunderstorms—Part 1

Remember to add data to your table for experiment 7.1. Read pages 183–186. Use the concept map below to help you organize the new information you will read.

All thunderstorms start with an

which pulls warm, moist air into the atmosphere, causing this kind of cloud to form

**This is also the name given to the stage the thunderstorm is in.
The next phase is called the**

**which consists of heavy rain, wind, lightning, and thunder.
The downward rush of air is called**

**which eventually overpower the updrafts.
This marks the last stage of a thunderstorm, called the**

Thunderstorms—Part 2

Remember to add data to your table for experiment 7.1. Read pages 186–189 in the text. Complete experiment 8.1 and fill in the lab report. Then answer "On Your Own" questions 8.3–8.5.

ON YOUR OWN

8.3 If a thunderstorm produces hail, in which stage of the thunderstorm would it come?

ON YOUR OWN

8.4 A thunderstorm begins, raining heavy sheets of rain for more than an hour before the rain begins to lighten. Was this thunderstorm composed of one cell or many cells?

ON YOUR OWN

8.5 Survivors of lightning strikes say that just before the lightning hit, their hair stood up. Why does that happen?

Tornadoes and Hurricanes

Remember to add data to your table for experiment 7.1. Read pages 190–194 in the text. Learn more about tornadoes and hurricanes by completing the "Digging Deeper" section. Then answer "On Your Own" questions 8.6–8.7.

DIGGING DEEPER
Tornadoes and Hurricanes

Check out the sites below for some very interesting information about tornadoes and hurricanes. There is a great video from National Geographic showing some really cool tornado footage.

link.apologia.com/ECPS2N/8.1
link.apologia.com/ECPS2N/8.2

Use the space below to write two interesting facts that you didn't know before about tornadoes and hurricanes.

_____

_____

_____

_____

ON YOUR OWN

8.6 The early warning stage of a tornado is called a "funnel cloud." This is a cone-shaped extension of a cloud that is pointed toward the ground. When a small funnel cloud that is still high off the ground is spotted, which stage is the tornado in?

ON YOUR OWN

8.7 Suppose you are unfortunate enough to be caught in a hurricane. The winds are blowing, the rain is coming down, and water is everywhere. Suddenly, it is sunny and calm. Is the hurricane over? How do you know?

Weather Maps and Weather Prediction

Remember to add data to your table for experiment 7.1. Read pages 194–197 in the text. Identify the parts of the weather map below. Then answer "On Your Own" questions 8.8–8.10.

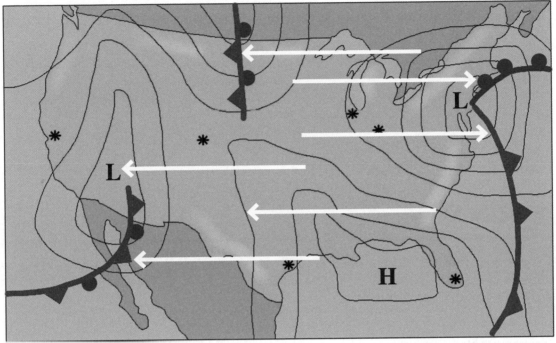

Illustration: Megan Whitaker

ON YOUR OWN

8.8 Ground-based temperature measurements tend to be made near places where people live, whereas satellite temperature measurements cover essentially the whole earth. Would you expect the average temperature of the earth as calculated by ground-based measurements to be higher than or lower than that calculated by satellite measurements? As time moves on and cities get larger, would you expect the difference between satellite measurements and ground-based measurements to be the same or increase?

ON YOUR OWN

8.9 Based on figure 8.10, would you expect to experience higher or lower atmospheric pressure if you left San Francisco and started heading east?

ON YOUR OWN

8.10 Based on figure 8.10, where will the occluded front be in the next few days: Mexico or Denver?

Interpreting the Results of Experiment 7.1 &
Making Your Own Weather Predictions—Part 1

Read page 198 in the text. Complete experiment 7.1 as directed in the text.

Interpreting the Results of Experiment 7.1 &
Making Your Own Weather Predictions—Part 2

Read page 199 in the text. Begin experiment 8.2 today and continue adding data for the next week (until you complete this module) in the data table of your lab report. Make sure to look back at your previous data table to determine any trends that you can use to make your predictions. Then complete the results and conclusions sections of the lab report before you start module 9.

Complete the study guide questions and have your parent correct them. If you need additional practice, you may wish to complete the optional summary for this module, located in the summary section of this notebook. Take time to understand anything that you may have missed and review your notes before taking the test for this module.

Study Guide

1 Write out the definitions for the following terms:

    a. Updraft

    b. Insulator

2 Both the Bergeron process and the collision-coalescence process explain precipitation, but each begins with a different kind of cloud. With what kind of cloud does each theory begin?

3 Which of the two theories of precipitation governs the fall of rain from the top of a cumulonimbus cloud? What kind of rain cloud would be the most likely described by the collision-coalescence process?

4 What is the difference between drizzle and rain?

5 What are the differences among sleet, hail, and freezing rain?

6 A meteorologist measures the dew point on two different mornings. The first morning is very humid, and the atmospheric pressure is high. The second morning is not nearly as humid, and the atmospheric pressure has fallen. On which day will the dew point be coldest? Why?

7 Name the three stages of a thunderstorm cell in the order they occur. At each stage, indicate whether an updraft, downdraft, or both are present. Also, indicate whether or not precipitation occurs.

8 If the heavy rain of a thunderstorm lasts for than 30 minutes, what can you conclude about its makeup?

9 Lightning forms as a result of electrical charge imbalance. Where does that charge imbalance originate and why does it occur?

10 Which is responsible for most of the light and sound in a lightning bolt: the stepped leader or the return stroke?

11 Where does the thunder in a thunderstorm come from?

12 Why do lightning bolts tend to strike targets that are high?

13 What is the difference between sheet lightning and a lightning bolt?

 14 What kind of cloud is necessary for tornado formation?

 15 List the five stages of a tornado in order. At which stage is the tornado most destructive?

 16 What are the four classifications that lead to a hurricane? What is used to determine which classification a storm fits in?

 17 What are the conditions in the eye of a hurricane?

 18 What causes a hurricane in the Southern Hemisphere to rotate in a different direction than a hurricane in the Northern Hemisphere?

Given the following weather map, answer questions 19–24:

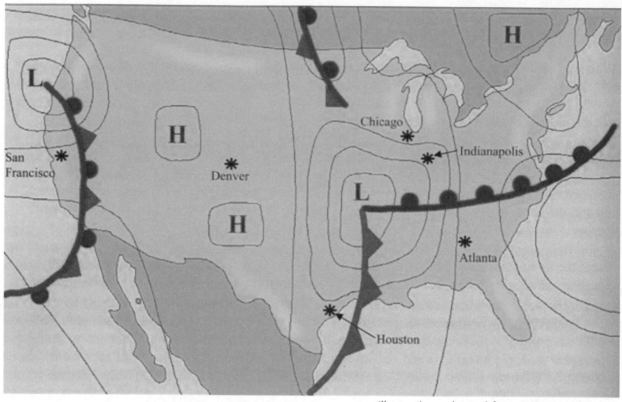

Illustration adapted from Megan Whitaker

19 Is the atmospheric pressure in Houston higher than, lower than, or nearly equivalent to that of Chicago?

20 Is the atmospheric pressure in Houston higher than, lower than, or equivalent to that of Atlanta?

21 Is the occluded front nearer to San Francisco or Canada?

22 Will Atlanta or Indianapolis be in for some warmer weather soon?

23 At the time this map was drawn, what city drawn on the map might be experiencing thunderstorms?

24 What city probably experienced long rains followed by thunderstorms recently?

MODULE 9

An Introduction to the Physics of Motion

Introduction & Mechanics—The Study of Motion, Forces, and Energy

Read pages 203–205 in the text. In the space below, explain in your own words what "all motion is relative" means. Make sure to include a description of a reference point in your explanation. Then answer "On Your Own" question 9.1.

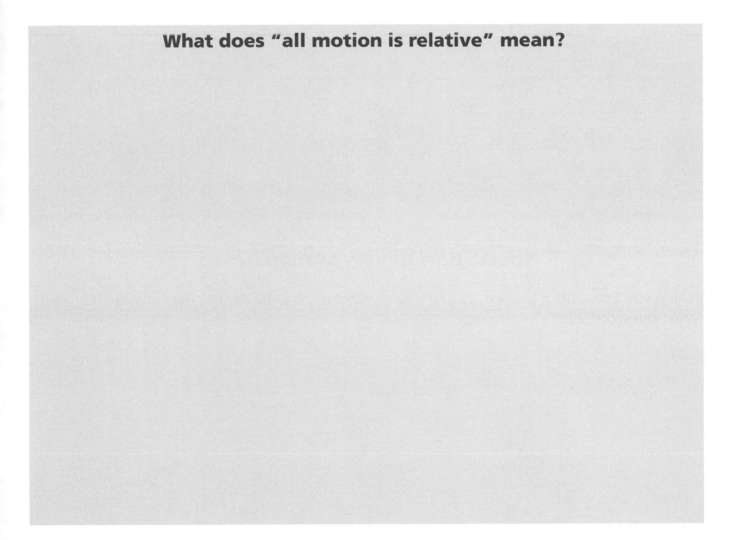

What does "all motion is relative" mean?

ON YOUR OWN

9.1 Suppose you go to a department store that has two floors, and you stand still on an escalator (a moving stairway) that allows you to travel to the second floor. Perhaps because you are a shady-looking character, three security guards are watching you. The first one is on the escalator with you, also standing still. The second one is standing still on the first floor near the escalator but not on the escalator. The third is standing still on the other escalator that is moving down. Relative to which security guard(s) are you in motion? Relative to which security guard(s) are you not in motion?

Speed: How Quickly Motion Occurs

Read pages 206–208 in the text, paying careful attention to example 9.1. Then answer "On Your Own" questions 9.2–9.3.

ON YOUR OWN

9.2 What is the speed of an aircraft that travels 115 miles in 30 minutes? Put your answer in units of miles per hour. Show all your work.

ON YOUR OWN

9.3 When measuring the speed of a snail, a good unit to use is millimeters per minute. A snail takes all day (12 hours) to travel 5 meters. What is its speed in millimeters per minute? Show all your work.

Velocity: Speed and Direction

Read pages 208–212 in the text, paying careful attention to example 9.2. Complete experiment 9.1 and fill out the lab report. In the space below, explain the difference between the terms "vector" and "scalar" and give an example of each. Then answer "On Your Own" questions 9.4–9.5.

The difference between scalar quantities and vector quantities is:

ON YOUR OWN

9.4 circle any of the following quantities that could represent a velocity.

a. 123 km/sec

c. 24 miles/hour and slowing

b. 34 m/min east

d. 15 meters west

ON YOUR OWN

9.5 A plane is flying due east at 520 miles/hour. Another plane is 20 miles east of that plane, flying with a velocity of 650 miles/hour due west. What is their relative velocity? Show all your work.

520 miles per hour east

650 miles per hour west

Acceleration: The Rate of Change in Velocity

Read pages 212–218 in the text, paying careful attention to examples 9.3–9.5. As review, use the graphic organizer on the next page to write out the definitions of "speed" and "velocity," both in words and as a mathematical equation. (You may need to look back at the last two sections to review these terms.) Then add the definition of "acceleration" as you read this section. Finally, answer "On Your Own" questions 9.6–9.8.

	Words	**Mathematical Equation**
Speed		
Velocity		
Acceleration		

ON YOUR OWN

9.6 A child is sledding. He starts at the top of the hill with a velocity of zero, and 3 seconds later he is speeding down the hill at 12 meters per second. What is the child's acceleration? Show all work.

ON YOUR OWN

9.7 Once that same child reaches the bottom of the hill, the sled coasts over a long, flat section of snow. If the child's velocity when the sled starts coasting is 12 meters per second east, and the child coasts for 6 seconds before coming to a halt, what is the child's acceleration? Show all work.

ON YOUR OWN

9.8 A good runner can keep up a pace of 0.15 miles per minute for quite some time. If a runner starts from rest and settles into a velocity of 0.15 miles per minute south after 3 seconds of running, what is the runner's acceleration over that 3-second interval? Show all work.

The Acceleration Due to Gravity—Part 1

Read pages 218–221 in the text, paying careful attention to example 9.6. Complete experiment 9.2 and fill out the lab report.

The Acceleration Due to Gravity—Part 2

Read pages 221–223 in the text. Complete experiment 9.3 and fill out the lab report. Then answer "On Your Own" questions 9.9–9.10.

ON YOUR OWN

9.9 A ball is dropped from the roof of a house. If the ball takes 1.1 seconds to fall, how many feet tall is the house? Show all work.

ON YOUR OWN

9.10 In order to measure the height of a skyscraper, a person stands on the roof and drops a ball. The instant that he drops the ball, he yells to an observer on the ground. The observer starts the stopwatch. When the observer sees the ball hit the ground, the observer stops the stopwatch. From the time elapsed, the observer calculates the height of the skyscraper. List all experimental errors associated with this experiment.

Complete the study guide questions and have your parent correct them. If you need additional practice, you may wish to complete the optional summary for this module, located in the summary section of this notebook. Take time to understand anything that you may have missed and review your notes before taking the test for this module.

Study Guide

1 Write out the definitions for the following terms:

a. Reference point

b. Vector quantity

c. Scalar quantity

d. Acceleration

e. Free fall

2 If an object's position does not change relative to a reference point, is it in motion relative to that reference point?

3 A glass of water sits on a counter. Is it in motion?

4 A child is floating in an inner tube on a still lake. His position does not change relative to a tree on the shore. He watches two girls jog along the shore of the lake. The girls are keeping perfect pace with each other. Neither is pulling ahead of nor falling behind the other.

a. Relative to whom is the child in motion?

b. Relative to whom is the first girl in motion?

c. Relative to whom is the second girl not in motion?

5 What is the speed of a boat that travels 10 miles in 30 minutes? Please answer in miles per hour and show your work.

6 What is the speed of a jogger who jogs 6 kilometers in 45 minutes? Please answer in meters per second and show your work.

7 Label each quantity as a vector or scalar quantity. Also, identify it as speed, distance, velocity, acceleration, or none of these.

a. 10 meters   _____   _____

b. 1.2 meters/second² east   _____   _____

c. 3.4 feet/hour and slowing   _____   _____

d. 56 liters   _____   _____

e. 2.2 miles/minute west   _____   _____

f. 2.2 millimeters/year   _____   _____

8 A car and a truck are traveling north on a highway. The truck has a speed of 45 miles per hour, and the car has a speed of 57 miles per hour. If the truck is ahead of the car, what is the relative velocity?

57 miles per hour north

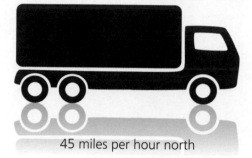

45 miles per hour north

9 If an object travels for 15 minutes with a constant velocity of 12 miles per hour west, what is the acceleration?

10 A sports car goes from a velocity of zero to a velocity of 12 meters per second east in 2 seconds. What is the car's acceleration?

11 A train takes a long time to stop. That's what makes trains so dangerous to people who cross tracks when one is near. If a train is traveling at 30 miles per hour south and takes 12 minutes to come to a stop, what is the train's acceleration?

12 A very picky physicist states that it is impossible for any object to experience free fall near the earth's surface. Why is the physicist technically correct?

13 Even though the physicist in question 12 is technically correct, why do we go ahead and assume that heavy objects are in free fall when they fall near the surface of the earth?

14 A long, vertical glass tube contains a feather and a penny. All the air is pumped out, and the tube is inverted, causing the penny and the feather to fall. Which hits the bottom first, the feather or the penny?

What is the height of a building (in meters) if it takes a dropped rock 4.1 seconds to fall from its roof?

 A hot-air balloonist drops a rock from his balloon. It takes 7 seconds for the rock to fall to the ground. What is the balloonist's altitude in feet?

 A scientist decides to study the acceleration of an object moving in a straight line. He measures the distance the object travels in 30-second time intervals. The scientist notices that in each interval, the object travels a shorter distance than it did in the previous interval. Is the direction of the acceleration the same as or opposite of the velocity?

Newton's Laws

Introduction, Sir Isaac Newton & Newton's First Law of Motion—Part 1

Read pages 229–234 in the text. Complete experiment 10.1 and fill out the lab report. Complete the graphic organizer below to help you remember the new information you will read about in

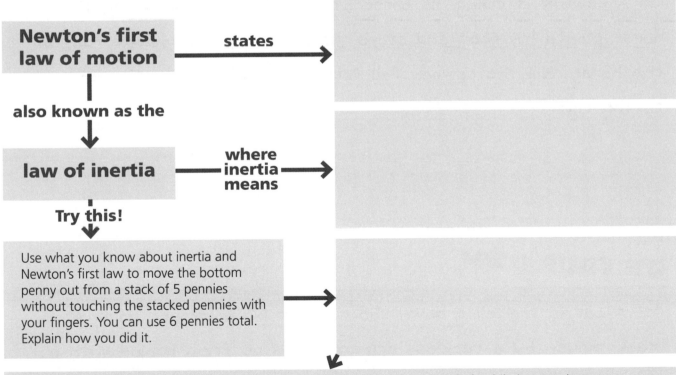

Newton's first law of motion — states →

also known as the ↓

law of inertia — where inertia means →

Try this! ↓

Use what you know about inertia and Newton's first law to move the bottom penny out from a stack of 5 pennies without touching the stacked pennies with your fingers. You can use 6 pennies total. Explain how you did it. →

↓

Now explain, based on the law of inertia, why it is a good idea to wear a seat belt while in a moving car. (You can use drawings to help explain.)

Newton's First Law of Motion—Part 2

Read pages 234–237 in the text. Complete experiment 10.2 and fill out the lab report. Complete the "Digging Deeper" activity and then answer "On Your Own" questions 10.1–10.3.

DIGGING DEEPER
Newton's First Law

To find out more about Newton's first law, check out the website below from the National Aeronautics and Space Administration.

link.apologia.com/ECPS2N/10.1

ON YOUR OWN

10.1 A cowboy is riding his horse at a fast gallop. Suddenly, the horse plants his feet and stops. As a result, the cowboy falls off the horse. Will the cowboy fall forward, backward, to the left, or to the right?

ON YOUR OWN

10.2 A car is traveling down the road at 30 miles per hour. A truck, driven by a reckless driver, comes up from behind with a speed of 50 miles per hour. The truck slams into the back of the car. Will the car's passengers be flung forward or backward in their seats?

ON YOUR OWN

10.3 A bomber is dispatched to drop a bomb on a factory. The figure below illustrates three points at which the bomb could be dropped as the plane travels from left to right. Assuming the bomb has no propulsion system of its own, at which point should the bomb be dropped?

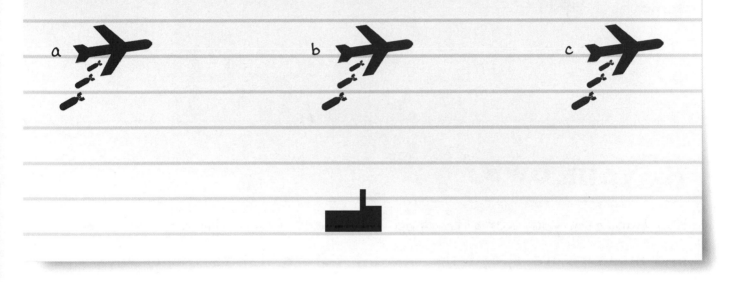

Friction

Read pages 237–240 in the text. Complete experiment 10.3 and fill out the lab report. Using the diagram below, explain why friction exists between two smooth objects in contact with each other. Then answer "On Your Own" questions 10.4–10.5.

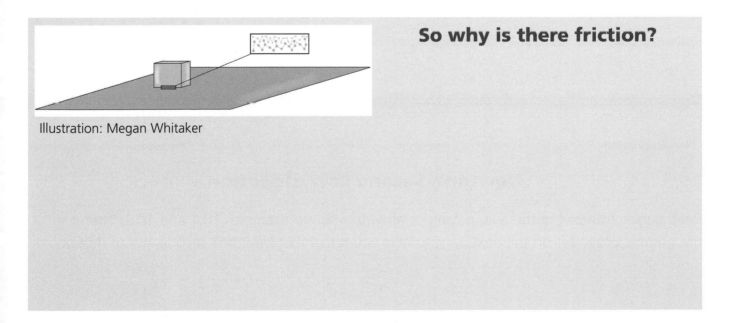

Illustration: Megan Whitaker

So why is there friction?

ON YOUR OWN

10.4 Look at the situation illustrated in figure 10.3. Suppose you wanted to push the box across the floor. If the box was filled with something really heavy, would you have to overcome more or less friction compared to a situation in which the box was filled with something light?

ON YOUR OWN

10.5 Suppose you were to drop an object from the top of a building and measure its speed the instant before it hits the ground. Suppose further that you did the experiment twice: once on a clear, sunny day and once during a thick fog. Would there be any difference in the speed of the object? If so, on which day would the object be faster?

Newton's Second Law of Motion

Read pages 240–244 in the text, paying careful attention to examples 10.1 and 10.2. Then use the graphic organizer on the next page to help you remember Newton's second law of motion.

Newton's second law of motion —— states ——→ [ ]

↓

It can also be written mathematically using the equation ——————→ [ ]

↓

which can be written as

↓

F = ma
...where...
F stands for the total force
m stands for the mass
a stands for acceleration

The standard unit of force is the

↓

[ ]

↓

which is equal to

↓

[_____]

↓

which is a mass unit multiplied by a distance unit divided by a time unit squared. Give two more examples of force units.

↓

[ ]

Static and Kinetic Friction

Read pages 244–246 in the text, paying careful attention to example 10.3. Use the graphic organizer below to make sure you understand the scientific vocabulary you will learn in this section. Then answer "On Your Own" questions 10.6–10.8.

CLASS OF FRICTION	DEFINITION	WHICH IS GREATER?
Kinetic friction		
Static friction		

ON YOUR OWN

10.6 A box (mass = 15 kg) is given an initial shove and allowed to slide across the floor with no person pushing on it. If the box slides north and experiences an acceleration of 1.1 meters per second² to the south, what is the kinetic frictional force between the box and the floor?

ON YOUR OWN

10.7 Suppose someone wanted to keep the box in question 10.6 moving at a constant velocity. What force must be applied in order to accomplish this feat?

ON YOUR OWN

10.8 A child wants to slide a block (mass = 10 kg) to the east. Static friction between the block and the floor is capable of resisting motion with a force of 30 Newtons west, while the kinetic frictional force is 20 Newtons west. What force must the child exert in order to get the block moving? If the block accelerates at 1.5 m/sec² east as a result of the child's force, what was the actual force used?

Newton's Third Law of Motion

Read pages 246–249 in the text. Complete experiment 10.4 and fill out the lab report. Complete the graphic organizer below to help you remember the new information you'll read. Then answer "On Your Own" questions 10.9–10.10.

Newton's third law of motion ——— states ———→

↓

Try this: blow up a balloon and let it go. Describe what happens, using Newton's third law. ————→

ON YOUR OWN

10.9 A tennis player hits a ball with her racket. The ball was traveling toward the player, but once she hits it with the racket, the ball begins traveling in the opposite direction. During the hit, the strings on the racket bow. what evidence do you have that the racket exerted a force on the ball?

what applied the equal and opposite reaction as required by Newton's third law?

where was the force applied?

what evidence do you have for this force?

ON YOUR OWN

10.10 An ice skater stands on the ice in his skates. He is holding a ball. Assuming that friction is so small it can be ignored, what will happen to the ice skater if he suddenly throws the ball hard to the west?

Complete the study guide questions and have your parent correct them. If you need additional practice, you may wish to complete the optional summary for this module, located in the summary section of this notebook. Take time to understand anything that you may have missed and review your notes before taking the test for this module.

Study Guide

1 Write out the definitions for the following terms:

    a. Inertia

    b. Friction

    c. Kinetic friction

    d. Static fricion

2 State Newton's three laws of motion.

3 In space, there is almost no air, so there is virtually no friction. If an astronaut throws a ball in space with an initial velocity of 3.0 meters per second to the "west," what will the ball's velocity be in a year? Assume there are no nearby planets.

4 A boy is running north with a beanbag in his hands. He passes a tree, and at the moment he is beside the tree, he drops the beanbag. Will the beanbag land next to the tree? If not, will it be north or south of the tree?

5 Suppose the situation in question 4 is now changed. The boy is running, but now his friend stands beside the tree with the beanbag. As the boy passes, he barely taps the beanbag, causing it to fall out of his friend's hands. Will the beanbag land next to the tree? If not, will it be north or south of the tree?

6 A busy shopper is driving down the road. Many boxes lie piled on the back seat of the car—evidence of shopping activity. Suddenly, the shopper must hit the brakes to avoid a collision. Will the boxes be slammed farther back into the back seat, or will they slam into the front seat where the driver can feel them?

7 When roads get wet, they can get slick. Obviously, then, the friction between a car's tires and the road decreases when the road is wet. Why?

8 In order to slide a refrigerator across the floor, a man must exert an enormous amount of force. Once it is moving, however, the man need not exert nearly as much force to keep it moving. Why?

9 A child is pushing her toy across the room with a constant velocity to the east. If the static friction between this toy and the floor is 15 Newtons, while the kinetic friction is 10 Newtons, what force is the child exerting?

10 A father is trying to teach his child to ice skate. As the child stands still, the father pushes him forward with an acceleration of 2.0 meters per second2 north. If the child's mass is 20 kilograms, what is the force with which the father is pushing? (Since they are on ice, assume you can ignore friction.)

11 In order to get a 15-kilogram object moving to the west, a force of more than 25 Newtons must be exerted. Once it is moving, however, a force of only 20 Newtons accelerates the object at 0.1 meters per second^2 to the west. What is the force that static friction can exert on the object? What is the force of kinetic friction?

12 Static friction can exert a force of up to 700 Newtons on a 500-kilogram box of bricks. The kinetic frictional force is only 220 Newtons. How many Newtons of force must a worker exert to get the box moving? What force must the worker exert to accelerate the box at 0.1 meters per second^2 to the south?

13 In order to shove a rock out of the way, a gardener gets it moving by exerting just slightly more than 100 Newtons of force. To keep it moving at a constant velocity eastward, however, the gardener needs only to exert a 45-Newton force to the east. What are the static and kinetic frictional forces between the rock and the ground?

14 Two men are trying to push a 710-kg rock. The first exerts a force of 156 Newtons east, and the second exerts a force of 220 Newtons east. The rock accelerates at 0.20 meters per second^2 to the east. What is the kinetic frictional force between the rock and the ground?

15 A child pushes against a large doghouse, trying to move it. The doghouse remains stubbornly unmoved. What exerts the equal and opposite force which Newton's third law of motion says must happen in response to the child's push? What is that force exerted on?

16 In a baseball game, a player catches a fast-moving ball. The ball stops in the player's hand. What evidence tells you that the player exerted a force on the ball? What exerts the equal and opposite force required by Newton's third law? What evidence does the player have for this force?

17 A man leans up against a wall with a force of 20 Newtons to the east. What is the force exerted by the wall on the man?

The Forces in Creation Part 1

Introduction, The Four Fundamental Forces of Creation & The Gravitational Force

Read pages 255–259 in the text, paying careful attention to example 11.1. (You may need to read it more than once to really understand it.) Complete the graphic organizer below to help you remember the new information you will read about in this section. Then complete "On Your Own" questions 11.1–11.2.

List the four fundamental forces from weakest to strongest and explain what they are.

FUNDAMENTAL FORCE	DESCRIPTION

Explain the principles of Newton's universal law of gravitation in your own words.

1

2

3

ON YOUR OWN

11.1 The gravitational force between two objects ($mass_1$ = 110 kg, $mass_2$ = 6 kg) is measured when the objects are 10 centimeters apart. If the 10-kg mass is replaced with a 20-kg mass, and the 6-kg mass is replaced with a 3-kg mass, how does the new gravitational force compare to the first one that was measured?

ON YOUR OWN

11.2 The gravitational force between two objects (mass₁ = 1 kg, mass₂ = 2 kg) is measured when the objects are 10 centimeters apart. The objects are then replaced with two different ones (mass₁ = 4 kg, mass₂ = 1 kg), and the distance is decreased to 5 centimeters. How does the new gravitational attraction compare to the first one that was measured?

Force and Circular Motion

Read pages 260–263 in the text. Complete experiment 11.1 and fill out the lab report. Complete the graphic organizer below to help you remember the new information you will read about in this section.

Describe centripetal force in your own words and then list the three general principles regarding centripetal force:

	DESCRIPTION
Centripetal force	
Principle 1	
Principle 2	
Principle 3	

A Fictional Force

Read pages 263–265 in the text. Use the space below to explain why centrifugal force is really a fictional force. Include examples. Then answer "On Your Own" questions 11.3–11.4.

Why is centrifugal force fictional?

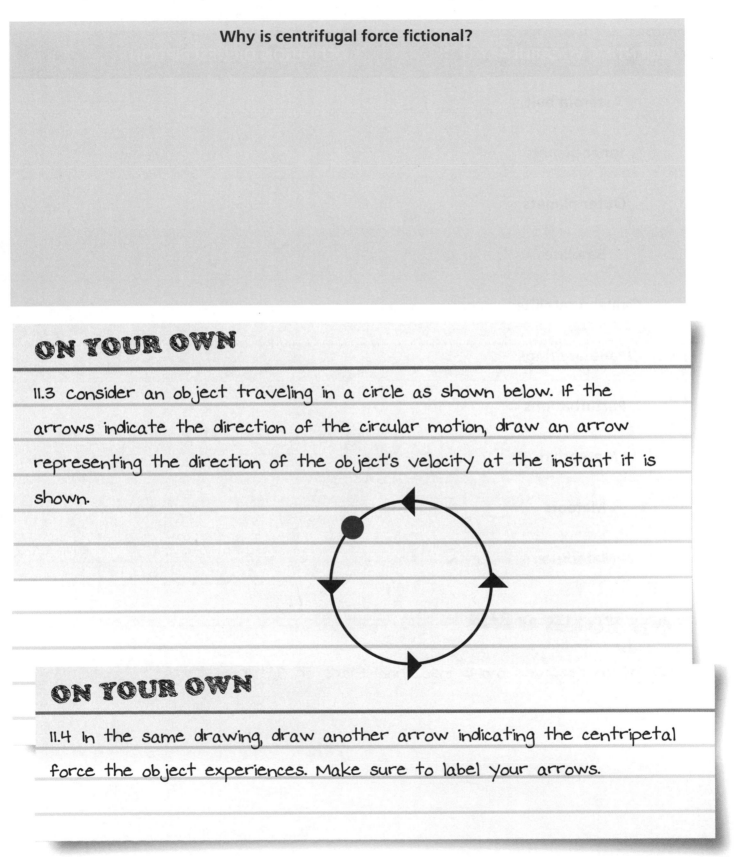

ON YOUR OWN

11.3 Consider an object traveling in a circle as shown below. If the arrows indicate the direction of the circular motion, draw an arrow representing the direction of the object's velocity at the instant it is shown.

ON YOUR OWN

11.4 In the same drawing, draw another arrow indicating the centripetal force the object experiences. Make sure to label your arrows.

The Gravitational Force at Work in Our Solar System

Read pages 265–269 in the text. To help you remember all of the scientific vocabulary you will learn, complete the graphic organizer below as you read. Then answer "On Your Own" questions 11.5–11.7.

SCIENTIFIC VOCABULARY	DEFINITION OR DESCRIPTION
Asteroid belt	
Inner planets	
Outer planets	
Satellite	
Galilean satellites	
Planetary rings	
Perturbations	
Meteoroids	
Meteors	
Meteorites	

ON YOUR OWN

11.5 Which receives more insolation: Mars or Saturn?

ON YOUR OWN

11.6 Saturn, Uranus, and Neptune have at least three things in common. List them.

ON YOUR OWN

11.7 A scientist analyzes a rock found in a nearby field. She says that based on its characteristics, it must have come from an asteroid. What should the scientist call this rock?

Comets & Hey, What about Pluto?

Read pages 269–273 in the text. After reading this section, use the graphic organizer on the next page to help you remember the scientific terms and descriptions you will learn about comets and dwarf planets. Learn more about comets by completing the Digging Deeper activity. Then answer "On Your Own" question 11.8.

SCIENTIFIC VOCABULARY	DEFINITION OR DESCRIPTION
Sublimated	
Nucleus of comets	
Coma of comets	
Tail & solar wind	
Short-period & long-period	
Oort cloud	
Dwarf planet	

DIGGING DEEPER
Comets

To find out more about comets, check out the "The Comet's Tale" website below and write down one fact you learn.

link.apologia.com/ECPS2N/11.1

ON YOUR OWN

11.8 The diagram below maps out two orbits around the sun. Which would most likely belong to a comet that would be relatively easy to see? Can the other orbit still be that of a comet?

a   sun   b

What Causes the Gravitational Force?—Part 1

Read pages 274–276 in the text. Complete experiment 11.2 and fill out the lab report. Use the drawing below to briefly explain Einstein's idea about planetary orbits.

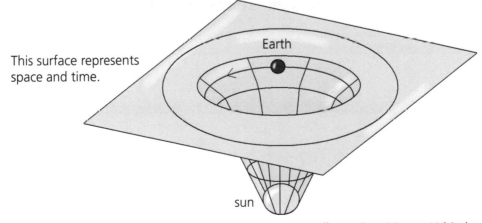

This surface represents space and time.

Earth

sun

Illustration: Megan Whitaker

What Causes the Gravitational Force?—Part 2 & A Brief History of Our View of the Solar System

Read pages 276–280 in the text. Complete experiment 11.3 and fill out the lab report. Then answer "On Your Own" questions 11.9–11.10.

ON YOUR OWN

11.9 If Einstein's general theory of relativity is true, how many forces are there in creation?

ON YOUR OWN

11.10 Suppose that a great physicist one day detected massive objects exchanging small particles with each other. That would not be conclusive evidence for the graviton theory. There is one other thing that must be shown to really provide conclusive evidence for the graviton theory. What is it?

Complete the study guide questions and have your parent correct them. If you need additional practice, you may wish to complete the optional summary for this module, located in the summary section of this notebook. Take time to understand anything that you may have missed and review your notes before taking the test for this module.

Study Guide

1 Name the four fundamental forces in creation. Which two forces are really different aspects of the same force?

2 Which is the weakest of the fundamental forces? Which is the strongest?

3 Name the three principles of Newton's universal law of gravitation.

4 The gravitational force between two objects (mass$_1$ = 10 kg, mass$_2$ = 6 kg) is measured when the objects are 10 centimeters apart. If the 10-kg mass is replaced with a 20-kg mass and the 6-kg mass is replaced with a 12-kg mass, how does the new gravitational force compare to the first one that was measured?

5 The gravitational force between two objects (mass$_1$ = 10 kg, mass$_2$ = 6 kg) is measured when the objects are 10 centimeters apart. If the distance between them is increased to 40 centimeters, how does the new gravitational attraction compare to the first one that was measured?

6 The gravitational force between two objects (mass$_1$ = 1-kg, mass$_2$ = 2-kg) is measured when the objects are 12 centimeters apart. If the 1-kg mass is replaced with a 5-kg mass, the 2-kg mass is replaced with a 4-kg mass, and the distance between the objects is reduced to 4 centimeters, how does the new gravitational force compare to the first one that was measured?

7 If Venus orbits the sun because the sun exerts a gravitational force on it, what is the equal and opposite force required by Newton's third law of motion?

8 What kind of force is necessary for circular motion? Give the definition of that force.

9 What are the three principles of circular motion?

10 In an Olympic event called the "hammer throw," an athlete twirls a massive ball on the end of a wire. Once he gets the ball twirling very quickly, the athlete releases the wire, allowing the ball to fly straight out into the field. The person who throws the ball the farthest this way is the winner.

   a. As the athlete twirls the ball faster and faster, will the wire have to apply more, less, or the same amount of centripetal force?

b. Suppose the athlete starts by gripping the wire close to the ball so the ball sweeps out a small circle. Then, keeping the speed of the ball constant, he allows some of the wire to slip through his hands so the ball sweeps out a larger and larger circle. Will the wire exert more, less, or the same amount of force as the athlete makes his adjustment?

 11 What is "centrifugal force"?

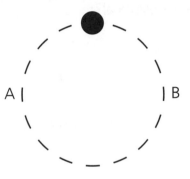 **12** In the following diagram, the ball is traveling from A to B along the path drawn. Draw the velocity of the ball and the force it experiences if it is traveling at constant speed.

A | | B

13 List the inner planets and the outer planets.

14 List the planets of the solar system from the closest to the sun to the farthest from the sun.

 15 List the planets that have rings.

 16 Where are most of the asteroids in the solar system?

What causes an asteroid to become a meteor?

 What are the three parts of a comet? Which of those parts is always present in a comet?

 During what part of a comet's orbit are all three parts present?

 Are comets' orbits circular or elliptical?

 Where do most physicists think short-period comets come from?

 What causes gravity, according to Einstein's general theory of relativity?

 What causes gravity, according to the graviton theory?

The Forces in Creation Part 2

Introduction, James Clerk Maxwell & The Electromagnetic Force

Read pages 285–289 in the text. Complete experiment 12.1 and fill out the lab report. Complete the graphic organizer below to help you remember the new information you will read about in

List three principles regarding electromagnetic forces.

1

2

3

ON YOUR OWN

12.1 For the diagrams below, draw a blue arrow to point out the direction of the force exerted on the red ball by the blue ball. In addition, draw a red arrow to indicate the direction of the force exerted on the blue ball by the red ball.

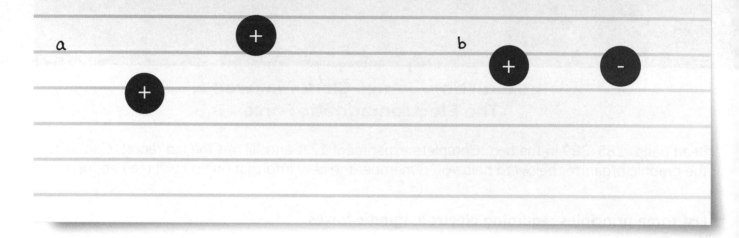

ON YOUR OWN

12.2 Two charged particles are placed 16 centimeters from each other, and the resulting force is measured. The charge on object 1 is then halved, and the charge on object 2 is divided by 4. The distance between the objects is also reduced to 4 cm. How does the new force compare to the old force?

Photons and the Electromagnetic Force

Read pages 290–291 in the text. Use the space below to explain in your own words what a photon is. Then answer "On Your Own" question 12.3.

A photon is...

ON YOUR OWN

12.3 A black object is heated until it glows with a nice, orange-yellow glow. If the black object has no net electrical charge, where does the light come from?

How Objects Become Electrically Charged

Read pages 291–295 in the text. Complete experiment 12.2 and fill out the lab report. Then complete the "Digging Deeper" section and "On Your Own" question 12.4.

DIGGING DEEPER
Electrostatic Induction

To learn more about charging an electroscope by induction, check out this website. There are a lot of interesting topics to check out using the navigation bar on the left. See how much you can learn about static electricity.

link.apologia.com/ECPS2N/12.1

ON YOUR OWN

12.4 If you want to give an object a positive charge but the only source of charge you have is negative, would you charge the object by conduction or induction?

Electrical Circuits

Read pages 295–299 in the text. Use the graphic organizer on the next page to help you remember the new information and scientific vocabulary you will read about. Then answer "On Your Own" question 12.5.

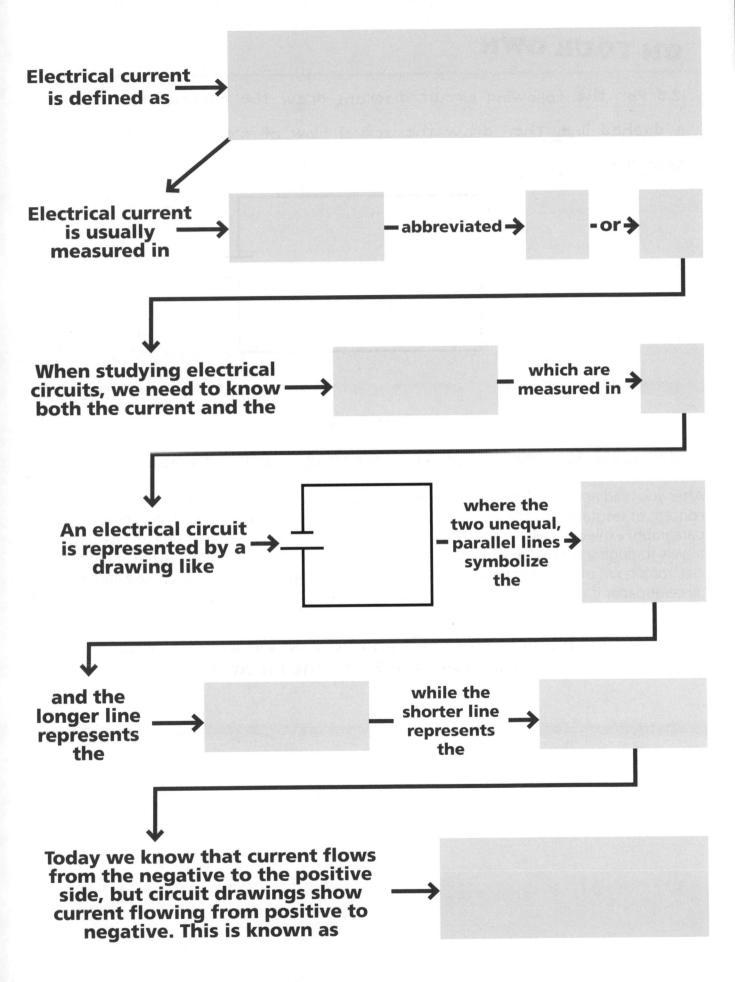

Electrical current is defined as →

Electrical current is usually measured in → ▢ — **abbreviated** → ▢ **- or** → ▢

When studying electrical circuits, we need to know both the current and the → ▢ — **which are measured in** → ▢

An electrical circuit is represented by a drawing like → ▢ — **where the two unequal, parallel lines symbolize the** → ▢

and the longer line represents the → ▢ — **while the shorter line represents the** → ▢

Today we know that current flows from the negative to the positive side, but circuit drawings show current flowing from positive to negative. This is known as → ▢

ON YOUR OWN

12.5 For the following circuit diagram, draw the current flow with a dashed line. Then draw the actual flow of electrons with a solid line.

Resistance

Read pages 299–301 in the text. Complete experiment 12.3 and fill out the lab report.

After you read and complete the experiment, explain what resistance is and how we use the concept of resistance in different metals in our everyday lives. Or write a short story (just a paragraph) explaining what happens to an electron as it leaves the negative side of a battery, travels through a light bulb, and goes back to the positive side of the battery. Write from the electron's point of view and pretend you're writing your story for a third-grader. (Use another piece of paper if needed.) Then complete "On Your Own" question 12.6.

**Resistance: What is it and how do we use it? ...or...
The Travels of Eddie the Electron**

ON YOUR OWN

12.6 When we work with most circuits, we assume that the resistance of the wire in the circuit is zero. Thus, the only resistance we consider is that of the device (or devices) in the circuit. Suppose a wire was made of aluminum. Would it have zero resistance? Hint: Think about the experiment you just did.

Switches and Circuits & Series and Parallel Circuits

Read pages 302–304 in the text. Draw an open circuit and a closed circuit in the space below and explain the difference. Next, use the Venn diagram on the next page to compare and contrast series and parallel circuits. Then complete "On Your Own" question 12.7.

Open circuit   **Closed circuit**

Series circuit   **Parallel circuit**

ON YOUR OWN

12.7 When strings of christmas tree lights were first produced, they were hard to use year after year because once a single light bulb on the string burned out, none of the lights would light up. Nowadays, if one bulb on a string of lights burns out, the others stay lit. what is the difference between the way strings of christmas tree lights used to be made and the way they are made now?

Magnetism & Permanant Magnets

Read pages 305–308 in the text. Complete the graphic organizer below as you read. Then complete "On Your Own" questions 12.8–12.10.

MAGNET VOCABULARY	DEFINITION
North & south poles	
Dipole	
Monopole	

ON YOUR OWN

12.8 Suppose you have two wires lying side by side. In one wire, the current flows one way, and in the other wire, an equal amount of current flows the opposite way. Could you wrap those wires around a nail and make a magnet?

ON YOUR OWN

12.9 A scientist studies the relative strengths of two magnets that are both made of iron and have the same size, shape, and mass. The scientist places the north pole of magnet 1 a certain distance from the south pole of a third magnet, which he calls the "standard magnet." He measures the attractive force between magnet 1 and the standard magnet. He then replaces magnet 1 with magnet 2, making sure it is the same distance from the standard magnet. The attractive force he measures this time is four times stronger than the attractive force he measured previously. What is the difference between magnet 1 and magnet 2?

ON YOUR OWN

12.10 Just like magnetic field lines, scientists also use electrical field lines to illustrate the force that exists between electrical charges. From what you learned about magnets, draw the electrical field lines that exist between the two charges as drawn below:

Complete the study guide questions and have your parent correct them. If you need additional practice, you may wish to complete the optional summary for this module, located in the summary section of this notebook. Take time to understand anything that you may have missed and review your notes before taking the test for this module.

Study Guide

1 Write out the definitions for the following terms:

    a. Photon

    b. Charging by conduction

    c. Charging by induction

    d. Electrical current

    e. Conventional current

    f. Resistance

    g. Open circuit

2 For the following situations, use a solid arrow to draw the force exerted by the circle with the solid line. Use a dashed arrow to draw the force exerted by the circle with a dashed line.

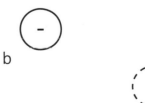

3 The force between the south pole of a magnet and the north pole of another magnet is measured. If the distance between the poles is increased by a factor of 3, how does the new force compare to the old one? Is the force attractive or repulsive?

4 Two charged particles are placed 10 centimeters from each other, and the resulting force is measured. The charge on object 1 is then doubled, and the charge on object 2 is left the same. Also, the distance between the objects is reduced to 5 centimeters. How does the new force compare to the old force?

5 What causes the electromagnetic force?

6 Given your answer to question 5, why don't charged particles glow?

7 If you were to use a positively charged rod to charge an object by induction, what charge would the object have?

8 If you were to use a positively charged rod to charge an object by conduction, what charge would the object have?

9 An electrical circuit uses a large voltage but a small current. Is the energy of each electron high or low? Are there many electrons flowing through the circuit, or are there few? Is the circuit dangerous?

10 Under what conditions is an electrical circuit reasonably safe?

11 Draw the conventional current flow in the following circuit:

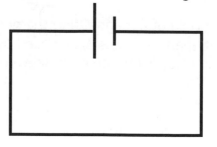

12 What is wrong with conventional current?

13 You have two wires. One is long, and the other is short. Other than that, they are identical. Which has more resistance?

14 You have two wires. One is thin, and the other is very thick. When the same current is run through each wire, which will get hotter?

15 In which circuit will the lightbulb glow?

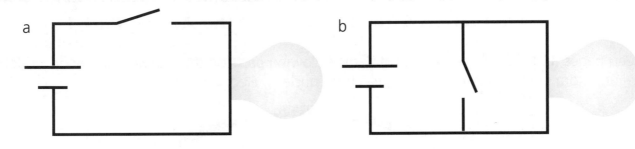

16 Three lights are in a circuit. When one burns out, they all go out. When the burnt-out one is replaced with a good light, the other two lights work again. Are the lights wired in a parallel circuit or a series circuit?

17 If it takes a flow of charged particles to make a magnet, where is the charged particle flow in a permanent magnet?

18 Is it possible to have a permanent magnet with only a north pole?

19 Is it possible to make a magnet from something that is not a magnet?

20 If a material does not respond to a magnet, what can you conclude about the atoms in that material?

159

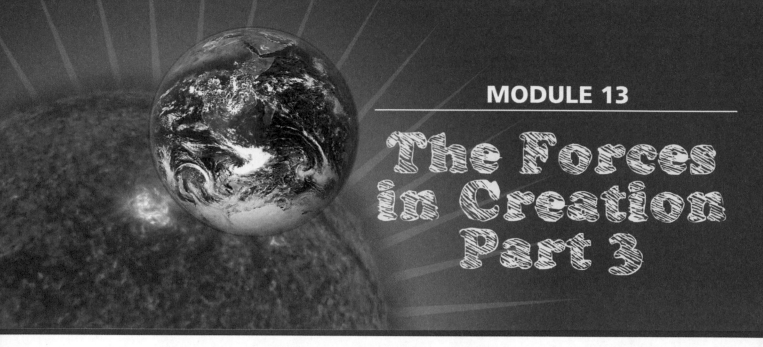

The Forces in Creation Part 3

Introduction & The Structure of the Atom—Part 1

Read pages 313–316 in the text. Identify the following parts on the drawing of a Bohr model of a helium atom below: proton, neutron, electron, nucleus, electron orbit.

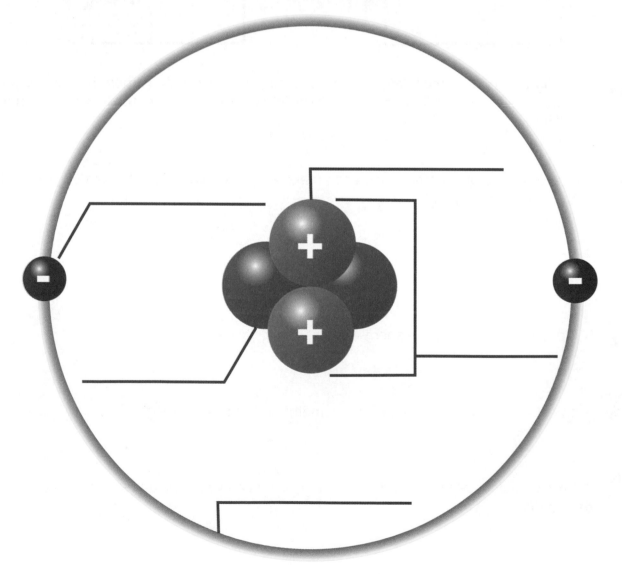

The Structure of the Atom—Part 2

Read pages 317–319 in the text, paying careful attention to example 13.1. Use the graphic organizer below to help you keep track of the scientific vocabulary you will learn. Then answer "On Your Own" questions 13.1–13.3.

ATOMIC VOCABULARY	DEFINITION OR DESCRIPTION
Atomic number	
Mass number	
Radioactive	
Isotope	
Element	

ON YOUR OWN

13.1 The element sodium is made up of all atoms with 11 protons. How many protons, electrons, and neutrons are in a sodium-23 atom?

ON YOUR OWN

13.2 All atoms with eight protons are oxygen atoms. If a particular oxygen atom has eight neutrons, what is its name and how many electrons does it have?

ON YOUR OWN

13.3 Of the following atoms, two are isotopes. Place an x in the box next to the isotopes.

- [ ] a. An atom with 16 protons, 16 electrons, and 17 neutrons
- [ ] b. An atom with 17 protons, 17 electrons, and 16 neutrons
- [ ] c. An atom with 16 protons, 16 electrons, and 18 neutrons
- [ ] d. An atom with 18 protons, 18 electrons, and 17 neutrons

The Periodic Table of the Elements

Read pages 320–325 in the text, paying careful attention to example 13.2. Use the graphic organizer below to help you keep track of the scientific vocabulary you will learn. Then answer "On Your Own" questions 13.4–13.5.

ATOMIC VOCABULARY	ALSO KNOWN AS	ALSO KNOWN AS
Bohr orbits		

Now draw the electrons on the proper electron shells for a sodium atom (^{23}Na). Use the periodic table of elements and table 13.1 to help you decide which orbits to use.

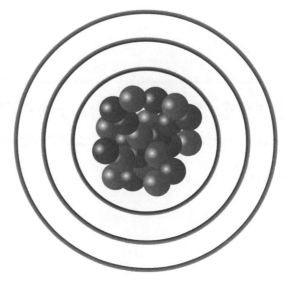

ON YOUR OWN

13.4 Draw a picture of a ¹⁹F atom, according to the Bohr model.

ON YOUR OWN

13.5 If you were to draw a picture of any isotope of cesium (Cs), what would be the largest Bohr orbit you would use and how many electrons would be in it?

The Strong Force

Read pages 325–326 in the text. Use the graphic organizer on the next page to help you keep track of the scientific vocabulary you will learn. Complete the "Digging Deeper" section to discover more about subatomic particles. Then answer "On Your Own" question 13.6.

ATOMIC VOCABULARY	DEFINITION OR DESCRIPTION
Nuclear force	
Pions	
Short-lived particles	
Quarks	
Gluons	

DIGGING DEEPER
The Strong Force

To learn more about the mind-blowing world of quarks and gluons, check out this "Particle Adventure" website by the Lawrence Berkeley National Laboratory:

link.apologia.com/ECPS2N/13.1

Click on the "Go" button for "The Standard Model" and follow the pages in order.

ON YOUR OWN

13.6 Suppose a new force is discovered, and scientists determine that it is governed by the exchange of a particle known as the "wileon." If the lifetime of a wileon is greater than that of a pion but shorter than that of a photon, what is the range of this new force relative to the range of the nuclear force and the electromagnetic force?

Radioactivity

Read pages 327–329 in the text. Use the graphic organizer on the next page to help you keep track of the scientific vocabulary you will learn. Then answer "On Your Own" questions 13.7–13.8.

The weak force governs a portion of a process called

⬇

which results from certain types of atoms called

⬇

This type of atom has a nucleus that is NOT

⬇

In order to make the nucleus more stable,
these atoms undergo a process called

⬇

of which there are three main types

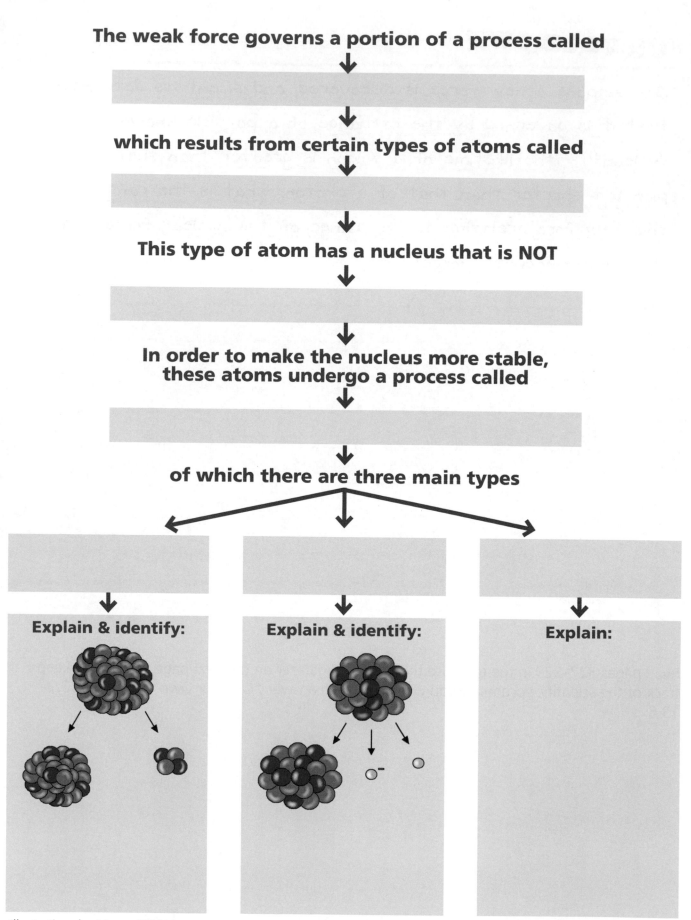

Explain & identify:

Explain & identify:

Explain:

Illustrations by Megan Whitaker

ON YOUR OWN

13.7 What is the daughter product that results from the beta decay of ^{90}Sr?

ON YOUR OWN

13.8 What is the daughter product of the alpha decay of ^{241}Am?

The Dangers of Radioactivity

Read pages 330–331 in the text. Use the space below to briefly explain in your own words how

How can radioactivity be dangerous?

ON YOUR OWN

13.9 People who regularly work with large samples of radioactive isotopes sometimes wear special suits lined with a thin layer of lead or other heavy material. What kinds of radiation are these people mostly protected against when wearing such a suit?

The Rate of Radioactive Decay & Radioactive Dating

Read pages 332–336 in the text, paying careful attention to example 13.4. Use the graphic organizer below to help you keep track of the scientific vocabulary you will learn. Answer "On Your Own" question 13.10 as you come to it in the reading.

ATOMIC VOCABULARY	DEFINITION OR DESCRIPTION
Half-life	
Radioactive dating	

ON YOUR OWN

13.10 The half-life of ^{131}I is eight days. If you start with a 40-gram sample of ^{131}I, how much will be left in 24 days?

Complete the study guide questions and have your parent correct them. If you need additional practice, you may wish to complete the optional summary for this module, located in the summary section of this notebook. Take time to understand anything that you may have missed and review your notes before taking the test for this module.

Study Guide

(Use the periodic chart to answer these questions. You will be able to use it on the test.)

1 Write out the definitions for the following terms:

a. Model

b. Nucleus

c. Atomic number

d. Mass number

e. Isotopes

f. Element

g. Radioactive isotope

h. Half-life

2 Order the three constituent parts of the atom in terms of their mass, from least massive to most massive.

3 What force keeps the protons and neutrons in the nucleus? What causes this force?

4 What force keeps the electrons orbiting around the nucleus?

169

5 What is an atom mostly made of?

6 An atom has an atomic number of 34. How many protons and electrons does it have? What is its symbol?

7 List the number of protons, electrons, and neutrons for each of the following atoms:

a. Neon-20 (Neon's chemical symbol is "Ne.")

b. ^{56}Fe

c. ^{139}La

d. ^{24}Mg

8 Two atoms are isotopes. The first has 18 protons and 20 neutrons. The second has 22 neutrons. How many protons does the second atom have?

9 Circle any of the following atoms that are isotopes.

^{112}Cd ^{112}Sn ^{120}Xe ^{124}Sn ^{40}Ar ^{120}Sn

10 Draw what the Bohr model says an ^{16}O atom would look like.

11 Draw what the Bohr model says a ^{25}Mg atom would look like.

12 What is the largest Bohr orbit in a uranium atom (the symbol for uranium is "U"), and how many electrons are in it?

13 Why is the strong nuclear force such a short-range force?

14 Determine the daughter products produced in the beta decay of the two radioactive isotopes shown below:

a. ^{98}Tc   b. ^{125}I

15 Determine the daughter products produced in the alpha decay of the two radioactive isotopes shown below:

a. ^{212}Bi   b. ^{224}Ra

16 A radioactive isotope goes through radioactive decay, but the isotope's number of protons and neutrons does not change. What kind of radioactive decay occurred?

17 The half-life of the radioactive decay of ^{226}Ra is 1,600 years. If a sample of ^{226}Ra originally had a mass of 10 grams, how many grams of ^{226}Ra would be left after 3,200 years?

18 The half-life of the man-made isotope ^{11}C is 20 minutes. If a scientist makes 1 gram of ^{11}C, how much will be left in one hour?

19 Why is radioactive dating unreliable in most situations?

20 List the three types of radioactive particles discussed in this module in the order of their ability to travel through matter. Start with the particle that cannot pass through much matter before stopping and end with the one that can pass through the most matter before stopping.

Introduction & Waves

Read pages 341–344 in the text, paying careful attention to example 14.1. Identify the type of wave shown below and label the parts of each wave. Then give the description of each wave type. Next explain what frequency is by defining the variables in the equation on the next page. Finally, answer "On Your Own" questions 14.1–14.2.

Type of wave: _____

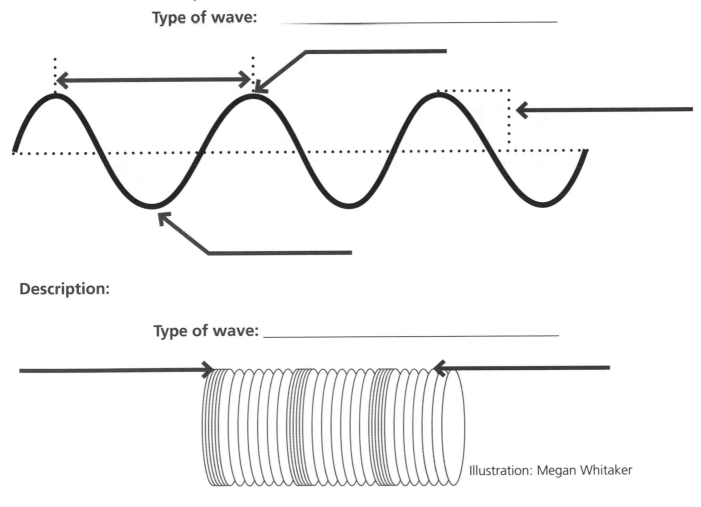

Illustration: Megan Whitaker

Description:

Type of wave: _____

Description:

f = v/λ where...	DEFINITION OR DESCRIPTION
f stands for	
v stands for	
λ stands for	

ON YOUR OWN

14.1 A longitudinal wave is suddenly stretched so that its wavelength is increased. If the speed of the wave does not change, what will happen to the wave's frequency?

ON YOUR OWN

14.2 Suppose you are wading on a beach that is experiencing waves that move with a speed of 0.5 meters per second and have a wavelength of 0.25 meters. If you stood still, how many waves would hit you every second? Show all work.

Sound Waves

Read pages 344–347 in the text. Complete experiment 14.1 and fill out the lab report. Then use the space below to explain in your own words what type of wave describes sound and why.

The Speed of Sound

Read pages 347–350 in the text, paying careful attention to examples 14.2 and 14.3. Complete experiment 14.2 and fill out the lab report. Use the graphic organizer below to help you remember the new information you will learn. Then complete "On Your Own" questions 14.3–14.4.

$$v = (331.5 + 0.6 \cdot T)\ \frac{m}{sec}$$

where "v" stands for

and "T" stands for

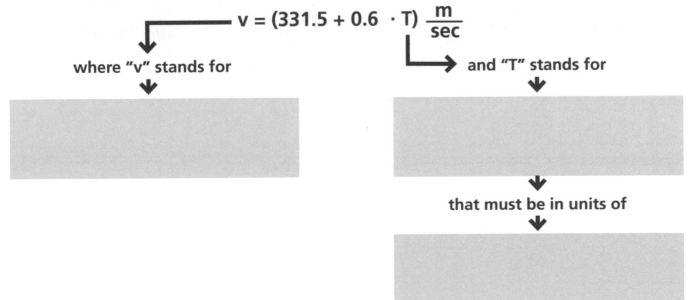

that must be in units of

ON YOUR OWN

14.3 What is the speed of sound in air when the temperature is 28 °C?

ON YOUR OWN

14.4 During a thunderstorm, the temperature is 18 °C. If you see a lightning flash and hear the thunder 1.5 seconds later, how far away did the lightning actually strike?

The Speed of Sound in Other Substances

Read pages 351–352 in the text. As you read this section, use the graphic organizer below to help you keep track of the new scientific vocabulary you will learn. Then complete the "Digging Deeper" section and "On Your Own" questions 14.5-14.6.

SCIENTIFIC VOCABULARY	DEFINITION OR DESCRIPTION
Supersonic speed	
Mach numbers	
Sonic boom	

DIGGING DEEPER
Mach Number

To learn more Mach numbers and how NASA names them, check out their site at:

link.apologia.com/ECPS2N/14.1

Now write below one fact you didn't know before reading this site:

_____

_____

_____

_____

_____

ON YOUR OWN

14.5 Remember from module 9 that the outer core of the earth is liquid but the inner core is solid. If a geophysicist is studying how sound waves travel through the core, would he expect the sound waves to travel faster in the inner core or the outer core?

ON YOUR OWN

14.6 A jet is traveling at Mach 1.8 when the temperature of the surrounding air is 0 ºc. what is its speed in m/sec?

Sound Wavelength and Frequency

Read pages 353–355 in the text. Complete experiment 14.3 and fill out the lab report. As you read this section, use the graphic organizer on the next page to help you keep track of the new scientific vocabulary you will learn. Then complete "On Your Own" questions 14.7–14.8.

SCIENTIFIC VOCABULARY	DEFINITION OR DESCRIPTION
Pitch	
Sonic waves	
Ultrasonic waves	
Infrasonic waves	

In the space below, explain the relationship between pitch and frequency.

ON YOUR OWN

14.7 Many flautists also play the piccolo, an instrument that looks like a very small, short flute. Which instrument (the flute or the piccolo) can produce notes with the highest pitch?

ON YOUR OWN

14.8 Are the wavelengths of ultrasonic waves shorter or longer than the wavelengths of sonic waves?

The Doppler Effect

Read pages 355–357 in the text. Complete experiment 14.4 and fill out the lab report. Complete the "Digging Deeper" section on the Doppler effect and then complete "On Your Own" question 14.9.

DIGGING DEEPER
Mach Number

To learn more about the Doppler effect and how you can use it to find the depth of a well, check out this site:

link.apologia.com/ECPS2N/14.2

Scientists use the Doppler effect to measure distances using sonar and radar. Find out more about that here:

link.apologia.com/ECPS2N/14.3

Write below some ways that scientists use the knowledge of the Doppler effect to help them study things.

ON YOUR OWN

14.9 Suppose experiment 14.4 were reversed. In this version of the experiment, the car sits still while your parent sounds the horn, and you run as fast as you can toward the car. Would the horn sound like it had a higher pitch, a lower pitch, or the same pitch as it had when both you and the car were standing still?

The Volume of Sound & Uses of Sound Waves

Read pages 357 362 in the text, paying careful attention to example 14 4. Use the graphic organizer below to keep track of the new scientific vocabulary you will be learning as you read. Complete experiment 14.5 and fill out the lab report. Then complete "On Your Own" question 14.10.

SCIENTIFIC VOCABULARY	DEFINITION OR DESCRIPTION
Bel	
Intensity	
Decibel	
Noise thermometer	

In the space below, explain how the amplitude of a sound wave affects the sound you hear.

ON YOUR OWN

14.10 The sound from a typical power saw has a loudness of 110 decibels. How many times larger is the intensity of the sound waves from a power saw as compared to those of normal conversation (40 decibels)?

Complete the study guide questions and have your parent correct them. If you need additional practice, you may wish to complete the optional summary for this module, located in the summary section of this notebook. Take time to understand anything that you may have missed and review your notes before taking the test for this module.

Study Guide

1 Write out the definitions for the following terms:

    a. Transverse wave

    b. Longitudinal wave

    c. Supersonic speed

    d. Sonic boom

    e. Pitch

2 In designing a car's horn, the engineers test the sound of the horn and decide that its pitch is too low. To adjust the horn, should the engineers change the electronics so as to produce sound waves with longer or shorter wavelengths?

3 A sound wave is travelling through air with a temperature of 30 °C. What is the speed of the sound wave?

4 If the sound wave in question 3 has a wavelength of 0.5 meters, what is its frequency?

5 A sound wave has a speed of 345 m/sec and a wavelength of 500 meters. Is this wave infrasonic, sonic, or ultrasonic?

6 A physicist takes an alarm clock and puts it in an airtight chamber. When the chamber is sealed but still full of air, the physicist is able to hear the alarm despite the fact that he is outside of the chamber. If the physicist then uses a vacuum pump to evacuate essentially all the air out of the chamber, will the physicist still be able to hear the alarm? Why or why not?

7 Are sound waves transverse waves or longitudinal waves?

8 You are watching the lightning from a thunderstorm. You suddenly see a flash of lightning, and 2.3 seconds later, you hear the thunder. How far away from you did the lightning strike? (The temperature at the time is 13 °C).

9 Sound waves are traveling through the air and suddenly run into a wall. As the sound waves travel through the wall, do they travel faster, slower, or at the same speed as when they were traveling in the air?

10 In the situation described above, what happens to the amplitude of the wave? Is the amplitude of the wave smaller, larger, or the same as the amplitude before the wave hit the wall?

11 A jet aircraft is traveling at Mach 2.5 through air at 1 °C. What is the jet's speed in m/sec?

12

A jet travels through air at 464.1 m/sec. If the air has a temperature of 0 °C, at what Mach number is the jet flying?

13 Why do jets travel at speeds of Mach 1 or higher only in sparsely populated regions?

14 A guitar player is plucking on a string. If he takes his finger and pinches the string to the neck of the guitar so as to shorten the length of the string, will the pitch of the sound emitted increase, decrease, or stay the same?

15 You hear two musical notes. They both have the same pitch, but the first is louder than the second. If you compare the sound waves of each sound, what aspect(s) of the wave (wavelength, frequency, speed, and amplitude) would be the same? What aspect(s) would be different?

16 The horn on your neighbor's car is stuck, so it is constantly blaring. You watch your neighbor get into the car and drive away from you, heading toward the nearest place for automobile service. Compare the pitch of the horn before he starts to drive away to the pitch you hear as he is driving away from you.

17 You are riding your bicycle toward a stationary police car with a siren that is blaring away. Will the pitch of the siren sound lower, higher, or the same as it will sound when you actually stop your bicycle? (Assume the actual pitch of the siren stays constant.)

18 You are standing near an interstate highway trying to talk on your phone. You have raised your voice because of the noise, so the loudness of your voice is about 80 decibels. The sound of the traffic on the highway is about 100 decibels. How many times larger is the intensity of the traffic's sound waves as compared to those of your voice?

19 An amplifier can magnify the intensity of sound waves by a factor of 1,000. If a 30-decibel sound is fed into the amplifier, how many decibels will come out?

Light

Introduction & The Dual Nature of Light

Read pages 367–370 in the text. Use the spaces below to explain in your own words what main theories describe light's behavior. Then answer "On Your Own" questions 15.1–15.2.

Particle theory

Wave theory

Quantum-mechanical theory

ON YOUR OWN

15.1 Which of the pictures below is the best illustration of the quantum-mechanical theory of light?

a.

b.

c.

ON YOUR OWN

15.2 Suppose a photon is traveling through air. If the particle suddenly hits a lake, what will happen to its speed?

Wavelength and Frequency of Light

Read pages 370–374 in the text. Label the electromagnetic spectrum chart below. Complete experiment 15.1 and fill out the lab report. Finally, answer "On Your Own" questions 15.3–15.4.

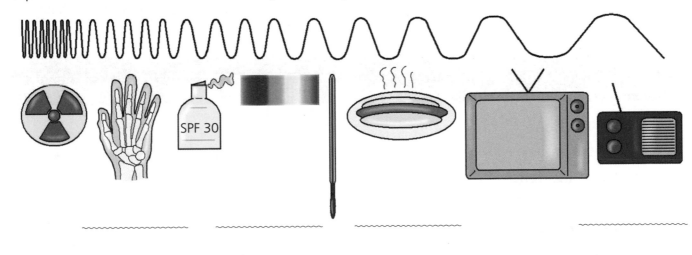

Illustration: Megan Whitaker

ON YOUR OWN

15.3 Without looking at figure 15.2 or figure 15.3, order the following colors in terms of increasing frequency: yellow, indigo, red, green.

ON YOUR OWN

15.4 If radio signals are really made up of electromagnetic waves, why doesn't a radio station's antenna glow when it transmits its signals?

Reflection

Read pages 374–377 in the text. Complete experiment 15.2 and fill out the lab report. Then complete the graphic organizer below to help you remember the new scientific vocabulary you will learn. Check out a fun application of the law of reflection by completing the "Digging Deeper" section. Then answer "On Your Own" question 15.5.

SCIENTIFIC VOCABULARY	DEFINITION OR DESCRIPTION
Reflection	
Angle of incidence	
Angle of reflection	

DIGGING DEEPER
Law of Reflection

To see how you can use the law of reflection when playing pool, check out this site:

link.apologia.com/ECPS2N/15.1

ON YOUR OWN

15.5 Draw the path of the light ray in the diagram below to show where the light eventually hits the screen:

Refraction

Read pages 377–383 in the text. Complete experiments 15.3 and 15.4 and fill out the lab reports. Then, identify the rays of refraction and the rays of reflection on the drawing on the next page. Then answer "On Your Own" questions 15.6–15.7.

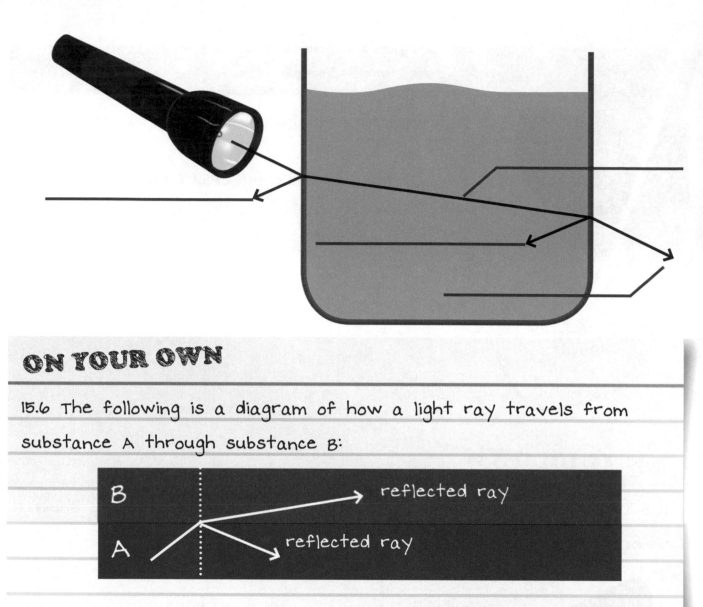

ON YOUR OWN

15.6 The following is a diagram of how a light ray travels from substance A through substance B:

B → reflected ray

A → reflected ray

Does light travel more quickly in substance A or substance B?

ON YOUR OWN

15.7 A man is spear fishing. He looks into the water and sees a fish in front of him. When he aims his spear, should he aim it at the fish, in front of the fish, or behind the fish?

Lenses

Read pages 383–385 in the text. Describe the differences and similarities between the lenses in the Venn diagram below. Then answer "On Your Own" question 15.8.

Converging Lens

Diverging Lens

ON YOUR OWN

15.8 consider the two lenses pictured below. which one focuses light rays closest to the lens?

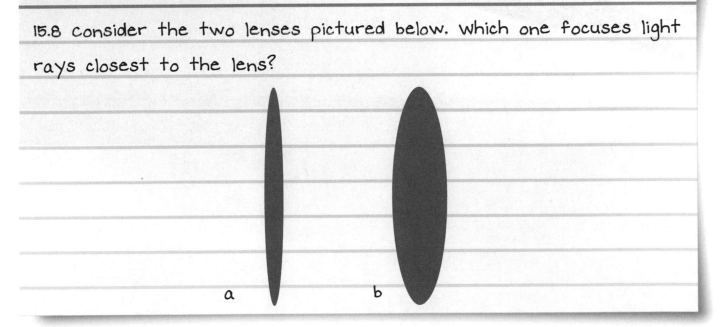

a   b

The Human Eye &
How We Perceive Color

Read pages 385–389 in the text. Complete experiment 15.5 and fill out the lab report. Then, use the space below to explain how your eye is like a camera. Make sure to discuss rods and cones. Then see what God's Word says about light in the "What Does God's Word Say?" section.

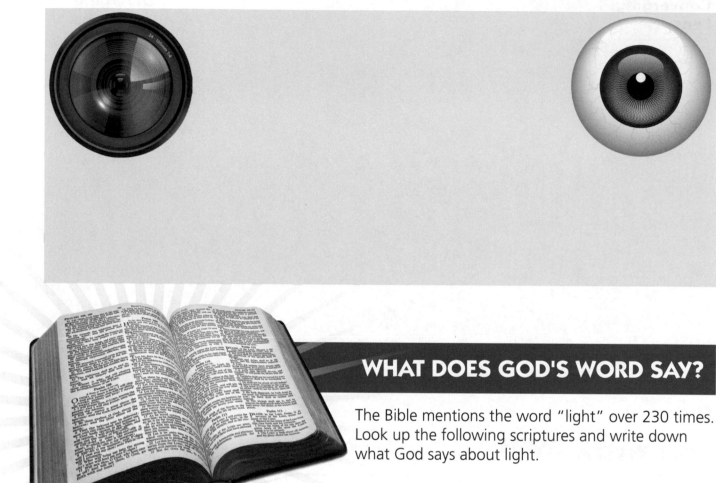

WHAT DOES GOD'S WORD SAY?

The Bible mentions the word "light" over 230 times. Look up the following scriptures and write down what God says about light.

Psalm 119:105

_____

_____

John 8:12

_____

_____

Matthew 5:16

_____

_____

Adding and Subtracting Colors

Read pages 389–392 in the text. Use the Venn diagram below to explain the difference between additive primary colors and subtractive primary colors. Then answer the "On Your Own" questions 15.9–15.10.

Additive Primary

Subtractive Primary

Colors

ON YOUR OWN

15.9 Suppose you have two flashlights. You cover the first with green cellophane and shine it on a mirror. When you look at the mirror, you see a green spot of light. If you were to then take the second flashlight, cover it with red cellophane, and shine it on the same part of the mirror on which the green spot is still shining, what color would you see?

ON YOUR OWN

15.10 Suppose you took a red shirt and put it in a dark room. Then, suppose you took a flashlight and covered it with green cellophane as described above. If you were to go into the dark room and shine the green cellophane-covered flashlight on the red shirt, what color would you see? Assume the dye on the shirt uses the subtractive primary colors to make its light.

Complete the study guide questions and have your parent correct them. If you need additional practice, you may wish to complete the optional summary for this module, located in the summary section of this notebook. Take time to understand anything that you may have missed and review your notes before taking the test for this module.

Study Guide

1 Write out the definitions for the following terms:

    a. Electromagnetic wave

    b. The law of reflection

2 Explain the wave theory of light, the particle theory of light, and the quantum-mechanical theory of light.

3 Sound waves cause air to oscillate. What do light waves oscillate?

4 What does Einstein's special theory of relativity say about the speed of light?

5 Light is traveling through water and suddenly breaks the surface and travels through air. Did light's speed increase, decrease, or stay the same once it left the water?

6 Order the following colors in terms of increasing wavelength: orange, violet, yellow, green. In other words, list the color corresponding to the smallest wavelength first, and end with the color that corresponds to the longest wavelength.

7 Order the colors in question 6 in terms of increasing frequency. Once again, start with the lowest frequency and end with the highest frequency.

8 Do radio waves have higher or lower frequencies than visible light? What about X-rays?

9 Infrared light is given off by any object that is losing heat. The human body is almost always losing heat to the environment. Why, then, don't human bodies glow at night, since they are emitting light?

10 Light hits a mirror, making an angle of 15 degrees relative to a line drawn perpendicular to the mirror's surface. What angle does the reflected light make with the same line? When light travels from one substance to another, what two things can happen to the direction of the light ray's travel?

11 In the diagram, will the man see his foot, despite the fact that the mirror does not reach the ground?

mirror

12 When light travels from one substance to another, what two things can happen to the direction of the light ray's travel?

13 In a physics experiment, a light ray is examined as it travels from air into glass. If the angle that the light ray makes with a line perpendicular to the glass surface is measured, will the refracted ray bend toward or away from that line?

14 When you look at objects underwater from above the water, they appear to be at a different position than their actual position. Why?

15 In order for you to see a rainbow, what three conditions must be met?

16 What is the difference between a converging lens and a diverging lens?

17 Which of the following lenses is a converging lens? Which is a diverging lens?

18 What is special about the way the eye focuses light as compared to the way a camera focuses light?

19 Suppose the cone cells on your retina that sense red light no longer work. If you look at a white piece of paper, what color would it appear to be? If you look at a red piece of paper, what color would it appear to be?

20 A shirt is dyed so that it looks violet. What colors of light does the dye absorb?

21 A cyan dye is made of a mixture of substances that absorb all light colors except blue and green. If you took a cyan piece of paper and placed it in a dark room and shined red light on it, what would you see? What would you see if you shined green light on it?

An Introduction to Astrophysics

Introduction & The Sun

Read pages 397–401 in the text. Use the graphic organizer below to identify the layers of the sun and explain what happens in each layer. Then explain what equation 16.1 tells us and what the variables mean. Finally, answer "On Your Own" questions 16.1–16.2.

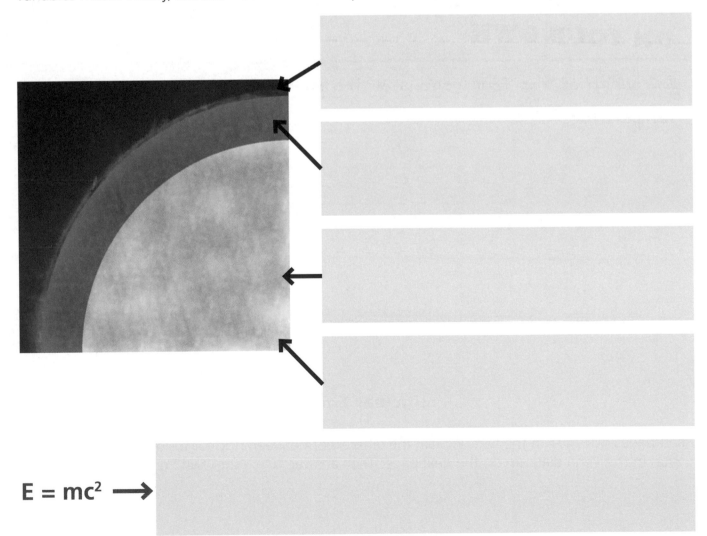

$E = mc^2$ →

ON YOUR OWN

16.1 As mentioned previously, the sun is mostly hydrogen and helium. As time goes on, will that composition change? If so, will the amount of hydrogen increase or decrease? What about helium?

ON YOUR OWN

16.2 Which of the four regions of the sun has the lowest temperature?

Nuclear Energy

Read pages 401–404 in the text. Explain the differences between nuclear fusion and nuclear fission in the Venn diagram on the next page. Then answer "On Your Own" questions 16.3–16.4.

**Nuclear
Fusion**

**Nuclear
Fission**

Energy
Production

ON YOUR OWN

16.3 In a nuclear physics experiment, two ^{7}Li atoms collide to form ^{12}C and two neutrons. Is this nuclear fission or nuclear fusion?

ON YOUR OWN

16.4 Suppose nuclear physicists discovered a fission process that always produced two smaller nuclei and only one neutron. Would this eliminate the danger of meltdown in a nuclear power plant? Why or why not?

Classifying the Stars in the Universe

Read pages 404–409. Explain the difference between absolute magnitude and apparent magnitude in the graphic organizer below. Complete the "Digging Deeper" section and then answer "On Your Own" questions 16.5–16.7.

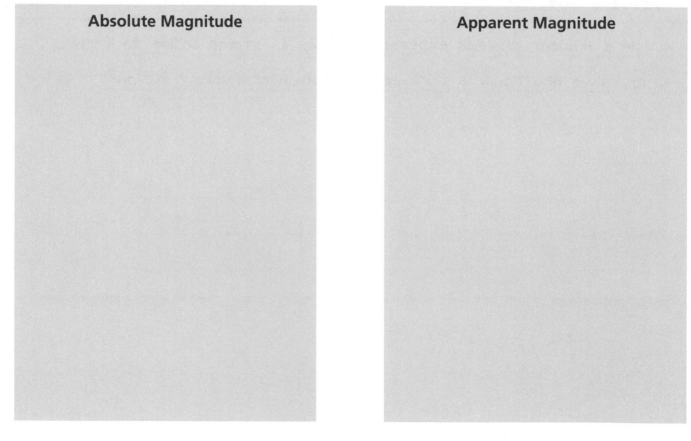

Absolute Magnitude

Apparent Magnitude

DIGGING DEEPER
Temperature and Constitution of Stars

To learn more about how scientists know the temperature and chemical makeup of stars, watch the demonstration and explanation that a science teacher gives at the link below:

link.apologia.com/ECPS2N/16.1

Use the space below to write one or two facts that you didn't know before:

_____

_____

_____

_____

_____

Use the H-R Diagram in figure 16.4 in the text to answer "On Your Own" questions 16.5–16.7

ON YOUR OWN

16.5 A star has a magnitude of 5, and its temperature indicates it has a spectral letter of F. What kind of star is it?

_____

_____

ON YOUR OWN

16.6 Is the star in the question above more or less massive than a star with a magnitude of 10 and a spectral letter of K?

_____

_____

ON YOUR OWN

16.7 Are red giants cooler or warmer than most white dwarfs?

Variable Stars

Read pages 409–411 in the text. Use the graphic organizer below to help you keep track of the new scientific vocabulary and information you will learn. Then answer "On Your Own" question 16.8.

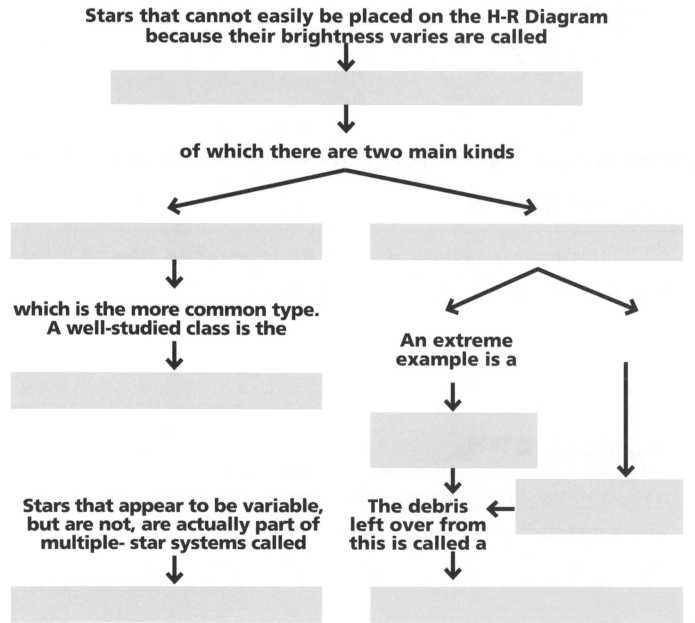

Stars that cannot easily be placed on the H-R Diagram because their brightness varies are called

of which there are two main kinds

which is the more common type. A well-studied class is the

An extreme example is a

Stars that appear to be variable, but are not, are actually part of multiple- star systems called

The debris left over from this is called a

ON YOUR OWN

16.8 Which kind of variable star would tend to exist for the longest time: supernovas, novas, or pulsating variables?

Measuring the Distance to Stars

Read pages 411–413 in the text. Use the space below to explain what a light year is and give a few examples of things measured in light years. Next, discover what God's Word says about stars in the "What Does God's Word Say?" section. Then answer "On Your Own" question 16.9.

Light year

WHAT DOES GOD'S WORD SAY?

God's Word has much to say about stars. Look up the following verses and write what Scripture tells us about one of God's brightest creations. Also think about what we can learn about the Creator of stars through these verses.

Psalm 8:3

_____

_____

_____

Genesis 1:14–15

_____

_____

_____

_____

Psalm 147:4

_____

_____

_____

_____

Psalm 19:1

_____

_____

_____

_____

_____

ON YOUR OWN

16.9 Which distance-measuring method is the most reliable: the parallax method or the apparent magnitude method? Why?

_____

_____

_____

Galaxies & An Expanding Universe

Read pages 413–418 in the text. Complete experiment 16.1 and fill out the lab report. Then use the graphic organizer below to help you remember what you learn by writing the definitions or descriptions in the appropriate spaces. Finally, answer "On Your Own" question 16.10.

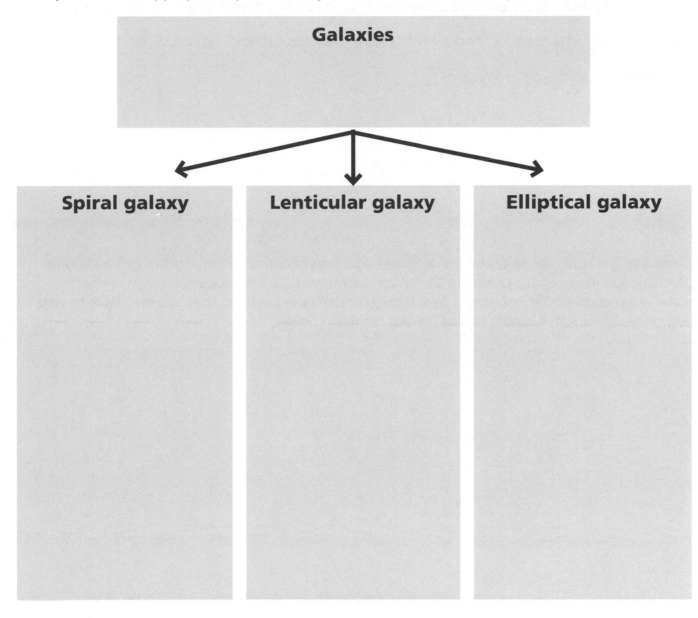

Galaxies

Spiral galaxy

Lenticular galaxy

Elliptical galaxy

Red shift

ON YOUR OWN

16.10 Assume that the universe is expanding, with Earth's solar system as its center. Suppose you were in a galaxy other than that of Earth. Would you still see a red shift from all the other galaxies in the universe? Why or why not?

Complete the study guide questions and have your parent correct them. If you need additional practice, you may wish to complete the optional summary for this module, located in the summary section of this notebook. Take time to understand anything that you may have missed and review your notes before taking the test for this module.

Study Guide

1 Write out the definitions for the following terms:

    a. Nuclear fusion

    b. Nuclear fission

    c. Critical mass

    d. Absolute magnitude

    e. Apparent magnitude

    f. Light year

    g. Galaxy

2 From the inside to the outside, name the four regions of the sun.

3 How does the sun get its power? In which region of the sun does this process occur?

4 What part of the sun do we see?

5 A ^{251}Cf nucleus is bombarded with a neutron. It breaks down into a ^{124}Sn nucleus, a ^{120}Cd nucleus, and seven neutrons. Is this nuclear fission or nuclear fusion?

6 Two ^{4}He nuclei collide and turn into a ^{7}Be nucleus and one neutron. Is this nuclear fusion or nuclear fission?

7 For both the nuclear fusion that occurs in the sun and the nuclear fission that occurs in a nuclear power plant, what can we say about the mass of the starting materials compared to the mass of what's made in the end?

8 Why is it impossible for a nuclear power plant to have a nuclear explosion?

9 Why is a nuclear fusion considered a better option for energy production than nuclear fission?

10 If nuclear fusion is a better option, why don't we use it?

11 Using the H-R Diagram on the right, classify the following stars:

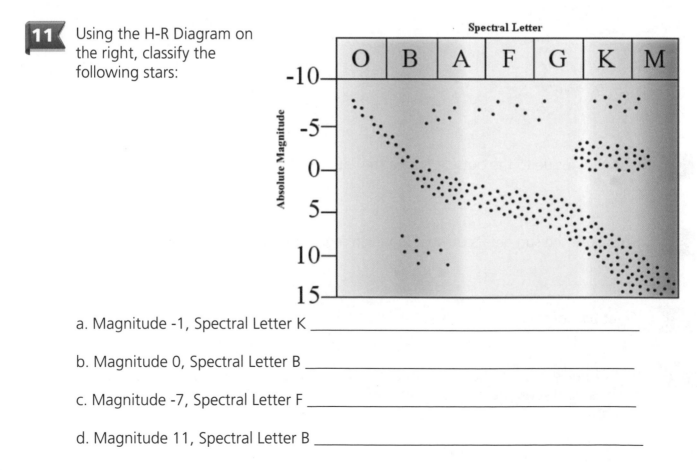

a. Magnitude -1, Spectral Letter K _____

b. Magnitude 0, Spectral Letter B _____

c. Magnitude -7, Spectral Letter F _____

d. Magnitude 11, Spectral Letter B _____

12 Which of the stars in question 11 is most like our sun?

13 Order the four stars in question 11 in terms of increasing size.

14 Order the four stars in question 11 in terms of increasing brightness.

15 Which of the stars in question 11 is the coolest?

16 What similarity exists among novas, supernovas, and pulsating variables?

17 What is the big difference among novas, supernovas, and pulsating variables?

18 What most likely formed the crab nebula?

19 What are the two methods for measuring the distance from Earth to a star? Which of the two is the most accurate? Which can be used to measure long distances?

20 Why are Cepheid variables so important for measuring long distances in the universe?

21 What are the four basic types of galaxies? To which type does the Milky Way belong?

22 Fill in the blanks: Stars group together to form _____, which group together to form _____, which group together to form _____, some of which group together to form _____.

23 For the first three answers you gave in question 22, give the names that apply to those in which Earth's solar system belongs.

24 Why do most astronomers believe the universe is expanding?

25 If the universe is expanding, does the geometry of the expansion matter? If so, why?

Experiments

"Get wisdom; develop good judgment."
Proverbs 4:5 (NLT)

Welcome to the most exciting part of your notebook! While it is important to learn about science, it is always more fun to *do* science. When you are reading your science text, you are studying important information gathered from scientists who came before you. You build upon that knowledge as you conduct your own scientific inquiry using the scientific method. In this section of your notebook, you will record your experiments.

Each of your experiments is designed to progressively build your confidence in understanding and using the scientific method. Lab report templates for each experiment listed in your text are included in this section to help you write a complete lab report.

Before you begin, you need to know that *science cannot prove anything*. Does that surprise you? It shouldn't. Scientific conclusions are continually being changed based on new information. Richard P. Feynman, a Nobel Prize winner in physics, said, "Scientific knowledge is a body of statements of varying degrees of certainty—some most unsure, some nearly sure, none absolutely certain." If the scientific method is used correctly, however, scientists can draw reliable conclusions. Thus, while the scientific method doesn't provide the process to *prove* something, it does provide the best method that allows you to construct consistent conclusions about the natural world.

When scientists begin to solve a problem, they follow a series of steps often referred to as the **scientific method**. These steps help ensure that they will have valid records and that their procedures can be duplicated (repeated) by anyone else who wants to conduct the same experiment. Why would that be important? Think about it. Science may not be able to prove something, but if the data repeatedly show the same result, it can be trusted.

The Scientific Method

Observe the World
The scientific method starts with **observation** and **research**. Scientists are aware of the world about them and study what others have learned before them.

Question the World
Observation and research usually lead scientists to ask questions about what they see. All scientific work begins with a question that can be answered with an experiment. This question is the **objective** (or **purpose**) of their experiment. Scientists state the purpose of their experiment as the first step in their lab report so that others know why they are conducting their investigation.

Formulate One Possible Answer to the Question
Scientists can test only one possible answer to a question at a time. This potential answer is called a **hypothesis** (or educated guess). After scientists have researched a subject and thought about the purpose of an experiment, they have a reasonable idea about what will happen. Scientists call this type of logic deductive reasoning. Have you ever read a mystery book? When you try to figure out "who's done it" based on the information in the story, you have created a hypothesis.

Experiment to Test the Hypothesis
It is important that the hypothesis can be tested and proven wrong. Remember that science cannot prove something to be right; it can only prove something to be wrong or build strong evidence that the hypothesis is reliable.

When scientists are designing an experiment, it is also important to keep as many factors as possible the same. These are called **control factors** because scientists control their consistency. If you try to grow a plant and you add fertilizer, extra water, and plenty of sun, can you tell which factor affected the plant's growth? There are too many **variables** (factors that change) in this example. Any one or a combination could affect plant growth. In scientific experiments, only one condition can vary.

Collect Data, Build Conclusions, and Share Results
Scientists record and interpret all the data they collect during an experiment. This is not always easy. Often the results from one experiment lead to many new questions. Finally, scientists share their **conclusions** about their results with other scientists so that knowledge can continue to grow. Now let's go have some fun!

"When a wise man is instructed, he gets knowledge"
Proverbs 21:11 (NIV)

Doing Experiments in *Exploring Creation with Physical Science*

When you come to each experiment in your reading, gather all of the supplies listed and set them out on your work table. Read over the procedure or instructions completely, thinking through how you will complete each step. Next read the procedure again, this time carefully completing each step in order as you read them.

In science it is very important to keep accurate, legible records of your experiments so that others can **replicate**[1] them. As you complete each experiment, fill out the lab report forms in this notebook. Use the following information about the sections on the lab report form to help you fill it out. Remember that neatness counts. Someone who has never read this book should be able to read your lab report and understand what you did and what you learned.

Objective or Purpose – In paragraph form, describe the purpose of the experiment. Why are you doing this experiment? What do you hope to discover or learn?

Hypothesis – After you think about the purpose of the experiment (and do a little research if necessary), you should be able to make an educated guess about what will happen. The hypothesis should answer a question that you can actually test in the experiment. Remember to write it as an "if/then" statement, such as "If I add salt to the water, then it will boil more quickly."

1. replicate – to do something again in exactly the same way

Materials – List all of the materials you actually used to perform the experiment. Do not just copy the list from the lab instructions because you may need or decide to make changes to the materials. Remember that in science it is important that someone else be able to replicate your experiment exactly, especially if you get interesting or unusual results. Remember to include details like the quantity or size of the materials when appropriate. If you are building something to conduct your experiment, it may be helpful to draw a picture of what you're doing so that someone else can understand and replicate your experiment.

Procedure – In your own words, and in complete sentences, write a paragraph explaining what you actually did to complete the experiment. It should be detailed enough that someone else can repeat what you did. You do not have to include things like "I wrote down the data in the data table" or "I cleaned up the materials." You should include any safety precautions or guidelines that will help someone replicating your experiment to avoid mistakes.

Data and Observations – Record all of the data that you collect during the experiment in a data table. This includes any measurements you make or numbers you count; remember to include units. You should also write down any observations that you make, such as what you see, hear, smell, or feel. Make sure that you don't include **inferences**[2] as your observations. Sometimes it is helpful to draw a picture of your observations to help explain what happened.

Results – This should be a sentence or two that explains what your data show, such as "The greater the amount of salt added to the water, the faster the water boiled until a certain amount of salt was added, and then any more showed no change in boiling time." Sometimes you can show your results in a table or a graph.

Discussion and Conclusions – This is the most important section of your report. Write a good paragraph (not just one or two sentences) explaining why you think you got the results that you did. Was your hypothesis supported? In other words, was your guess correct? If so, why do you think so? If not, why do you think it wasn't? What factors do you think contributed to your results? In other words, what were some things that could have caused errors? You should list several sources of possible errors in your experiment. You should also connect how this experiment and the lesson you are learning in the text relate. This section is used to make sure that you understand *why* you did the experiment as well as *how* you did the experiment.

2. inference – a conclusion drawn from an observation

SCIENTIFIC LAB REPORT
Experiment 1.1
Atoms and Molecules

Objective or Purpose

Hypothesis

Materials

Procedure

EXPERIMENT 1.1

DATA TABLE

OBSERVATIONS	WIRE 1	WIRE 2	SOLUTION
At beginning			
At 10 minutes			

Results

Discussion and Conclusions

SCIENTIFIC LAB REPORT
Experiment 1.2
Cubits and Fingers

Objective or Purpose

Hypothesis

Materials

Procedure

Data and Observations

DATA TABLE

Number of "fingers" in a "Cubit" _____ fingers

MEASUREMENTS	CUBITS	FINGERS
Table length		
Table width		

Conversion of table length from cubits to fingers:

Conversion of table width from cubits to fingers:

Results

Discussion and Conclusions

SCIENTIFIC LAB REPORT
Experiment 1.3
Concentration

Objective or Purpose

Hypothesis

Materials

Procedure

Data and Observations

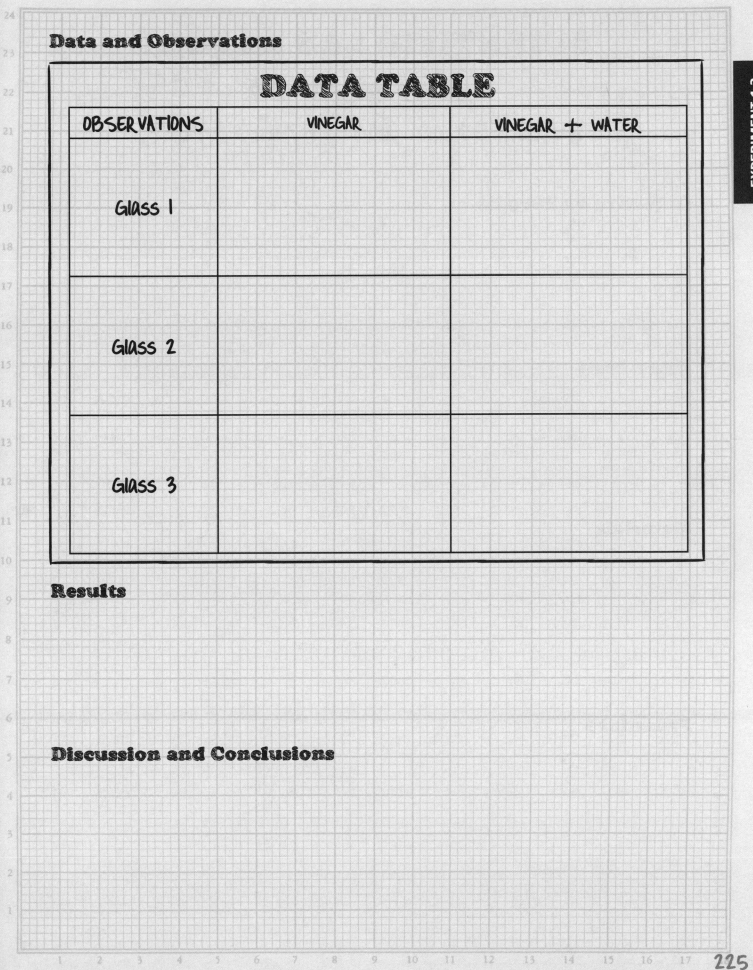

DATA TABLE

OBSERVATIONS	VINEGAR	VINEGAR + WATER
Glass 1		
Glass 2		
Glass 3		

Results

Discussion and Conclusions

SCIENTIFIC LAB REPORT
Experiment 2.1
Evaporation and Temperature

Objective or Purpose

Hypothesis

Materials

Procedure

Data and Observations

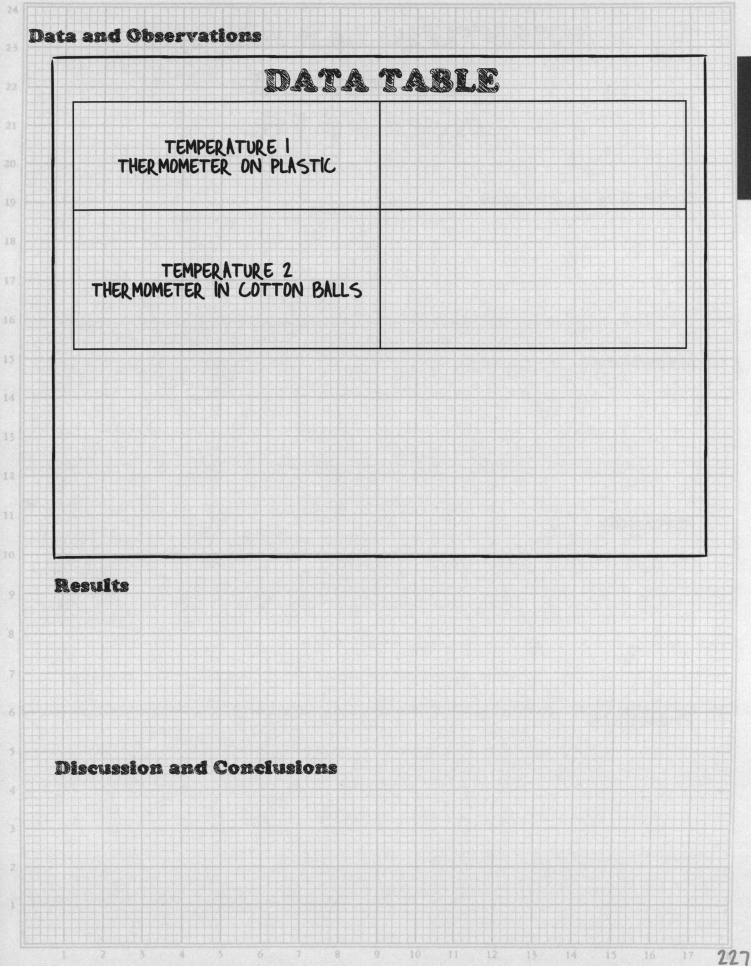

DATA TABLE

TEMPERATURE 1 THERMOMETER ON PLASTIC	
TEMPERATURE 2 THERMOMETER IN COTTON BALLS	

Results

Discussion and Conclusions

SCIENTIFIC LAB REPORT
Experiment 2.2
Oxygen and Fire

Objective or Purpose

To see what happens when
a lot of oxygen hits a flame.

Hypothesis

I think the flame will burn brighter
and spark.

Materials

glass Jar   a teaspoon
Candle   Eye protection
matches
2 cups hydrogen peroxide = HP
Bakers yeast
A Bottle
A Balloon

Procedure

△ Fill Bottle with HP

✳ Quickly add teaspoon of yeast

✳ Quickly Put Balloon over Bottle

✳ Shake Bottle gently

✳ While Balloon is filling with oxygen from HP + yeast
light candle, Put Jar over candle, See light go out because no oxygen.

✳ Take Balloon off, make sure
no oxygen comes out.

✳ Let oxygen out on candle flame
Slowly see what happens.

✳ Clean up.

Data and Observations

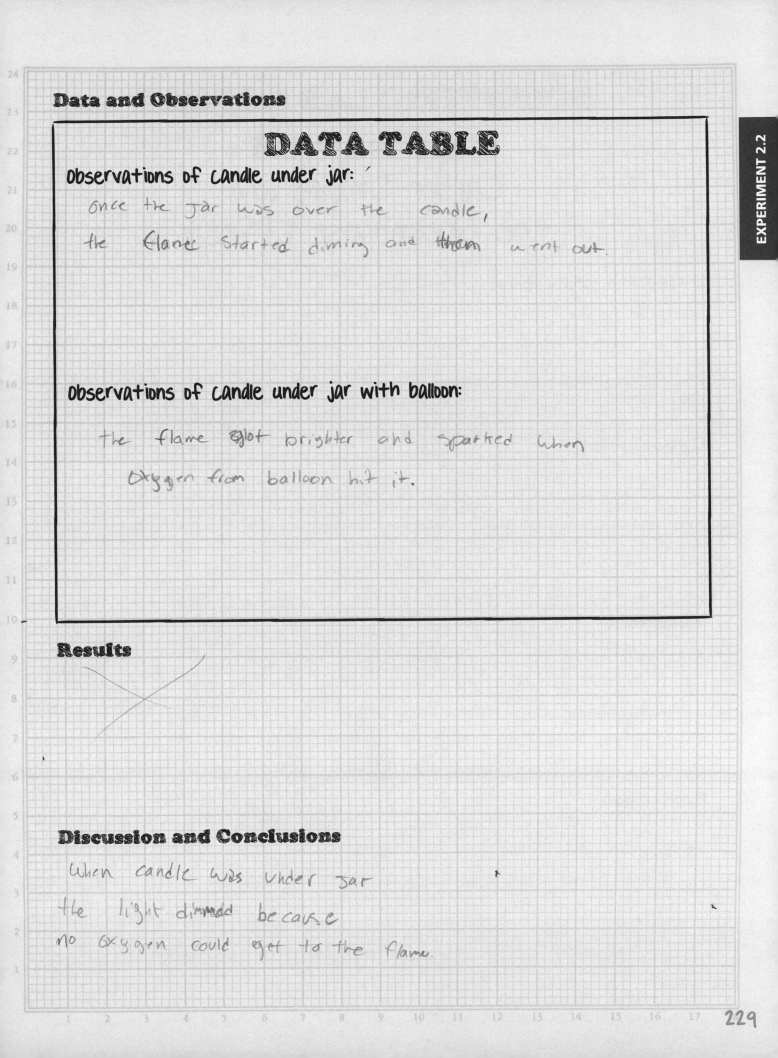

DATA TABLE

observations of candle under jar:

once the jar was over the candle,
the flame started diming and them went out.

observations of candle under jar with balloon:

the flame glot brighter and sparked when
oxygen from balloon hit it.

Results

Discussion and Conclusions

When candle was under jar
the light dimmed because
no oxygen could get to the flame.

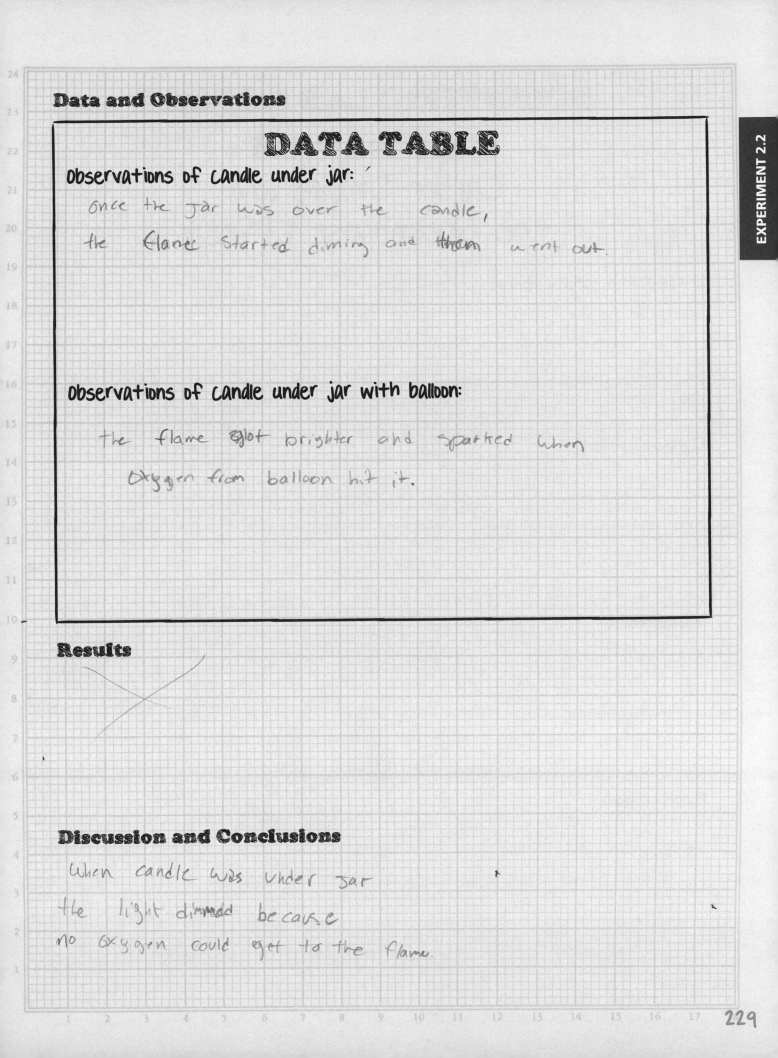
EXPERIMENT 2.2

229

SCIENTIFIC LAB REPORT

Experiment 2.3
Carbon Dioxide and
the Greenhouse Effect

Objective or Purpose

Hypothesis

Materials

Procedure

Data and Observations

DATA TABLE

TEMPERATURE A AIR	
TEMPERATURE B CARBON DIOXIDE	

Results

Discussion and Conclusions

SCIENTIFIC LAB REPORT
Experiment 3.1
Atmospheric Pressure

Objective or Purpose

Hypothesis

Materials

Procedure

Data and Observations

DATA TABLE	
UPRIGHT CAN	
UPSIDE-DOWN CAN	

Results

Discussion and Conclusions

SCIENTIFIC LAB REPORT
Experiment 3.2
Seeing the Effect of Changing Temperature

Objective or Purpose

Hypothesis

Materials

Procedure

Data and Observations

DATA TABLE

Before	After

Results

Discussion and Conclusions

SCIENTIFIC LAB REPORT
Experiment 4.1
The Chemical Composition of water

Objective or Purpose

Hypothesis

Materials

Procedure

Data and Observations

DATA TABLE

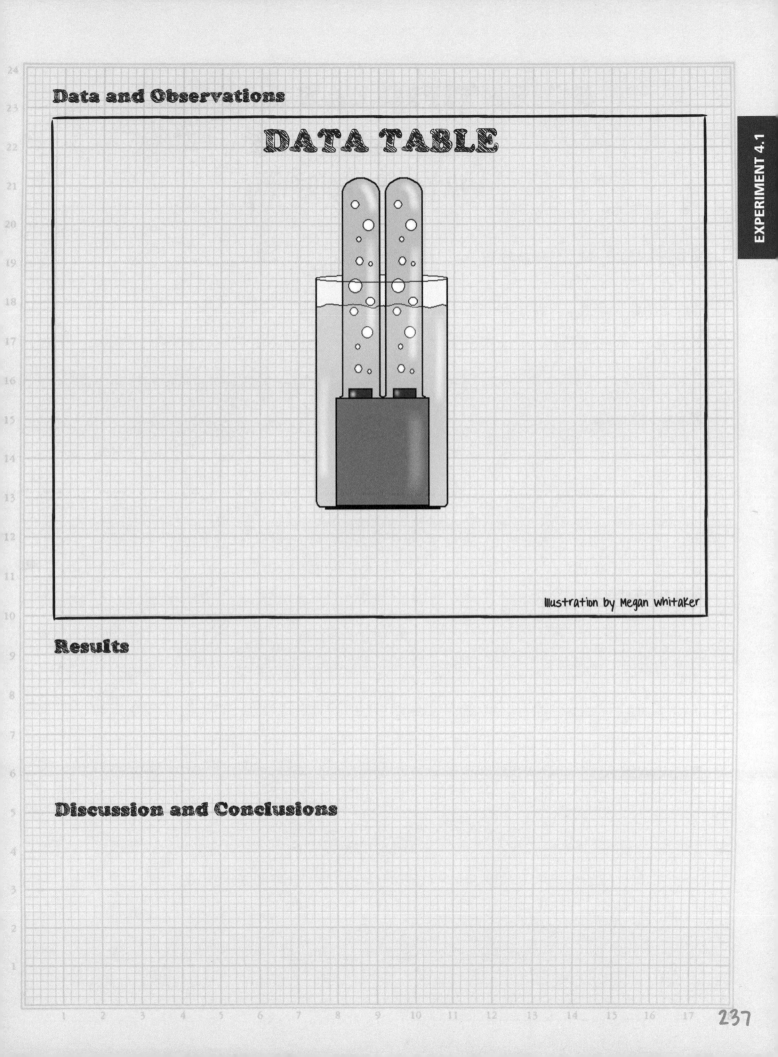

Illustration by Megan Whitaker

Results

Discussion and Conclusions

SCIENTIFIC LAB REPORT
Experiment 4.2
water's Polarity

Objective or Purpose

Hypothesis

Materials

Procedure

Data and Observations

DATA TABLE	
WATER	
OIL	

Results

Discussion and Conclusions

SCIENTIFIC LAB REPORT
Experiment 4.3
Solvents and Solutes

Objective or Purpose

Hypothesis

Materials

Procedure

Data and Observations

DATA TABLE

SUGAR IN WATER	
CANOLA OIL IN WATER	
TABLE SALT IN WATER	
OLIVE OIL IN WATER	
OLIVE OIL IN CANOLA OIL	

Results

Discussion and Conclusions

SCIENTIFIC LAB REPORT
Experiment 4.4
Comparing Solid Water to Solid Butter

Objective or Purpose

Hypothesis

Materials

Procedure

Data and Observations

DATA TABLE	
ICE IN WATER	
COLD BUTTER IN LIQUID BUTTER	

Results

Discussion and Conclusions

SCIENTIFIC LAB REPORT
Experiment 4.5
Water's Cohesion

Objective or Purpose

Hypothesis

Materials

Procedure

Data and Observations

DATA TABLE

Results

Discussion and Conclusions

SCIENTIFIC LAB REPORT
Experiment 4.6
The Forces between Molecules

Objective or Purpose

Hypothesis

Materials

Procedure

Data and Observations

DATA TABLE

Results

Discussion and Conclusions

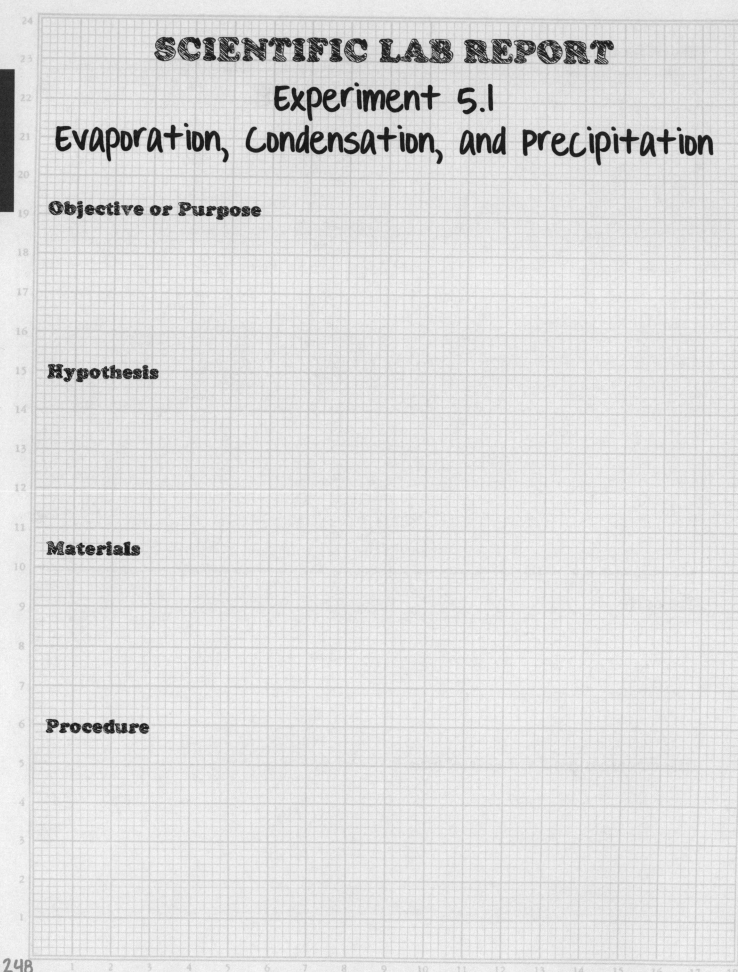

SCIENTIFIC LAB REPORT
Experiment 5.1
Evaporation, Condensation, and Precipitation

Objective or Purpose

Hypothesis

Materials

Procedure

Data and Observations

DATA TABLE

Results

Discussion and Conclusions

SCIENTIFIC LAB REPORT
Experiment 5.2
Ice and Salt

Objective or Purpose

Hypothesis

Materials

Procedure

Data and Observations

DATA TABLE

Results

Discussion and Conclusions

SCIENTIFIC LAB REPORT
Experiment 5.3
Cloud Formation

Objective or Purpose

Hypothesis

Materials

Procedure

Data and Observations

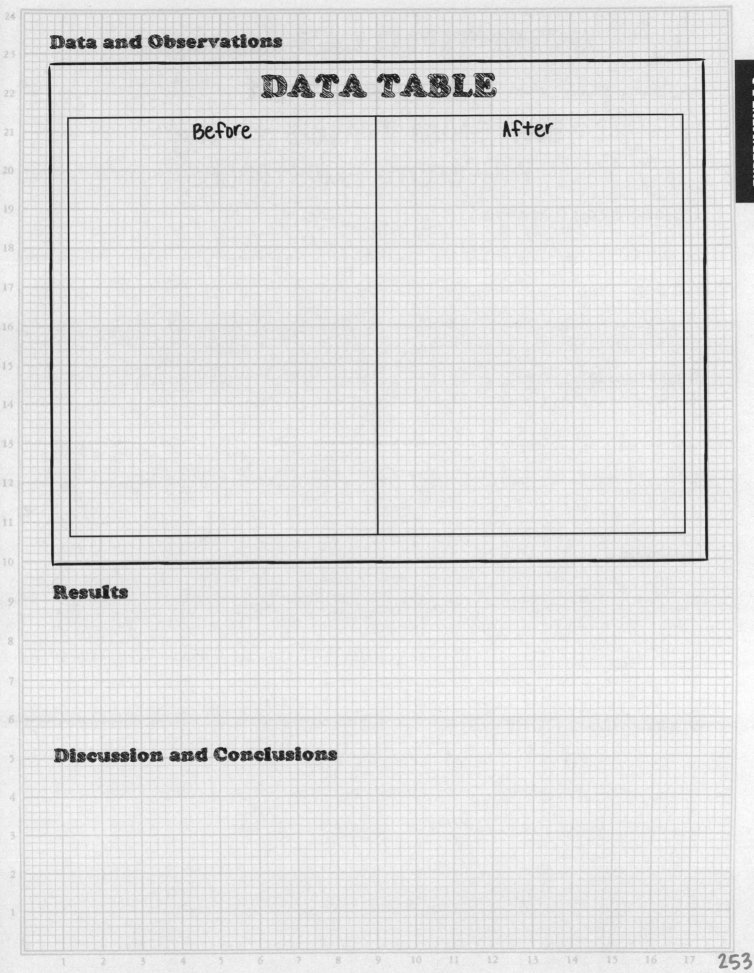

DATA TABLE

Before	After

Results

Discussion and Conclusions

SCIENTIFIC LAB REPORT
Experiment 6.1
How Sound Travels through Different Substances

Objective or Purpose

Hypothesis

Materials

Procedure

Data and Observations

DATA TABLE		
	OBSERVATION	COMPARISON
Spoons in air		
Spoons in air through string		
Spoons under water		
Spoons under water and ear under water		
Spoons under water through string		

Results

Discussion and Conclusions

SCIENTIFIC LAB REPORT
Experiment 6.2
A Simulation of Plastic Rock

Objective or Purpose

Hypothesis

Materials

Procedure

Data and Observations

DATA TABLE

Results

Discussion and Conclusions

SCIENTIFIC LAB REPORT
Experiment 6.3
Making an Electromagnet

Objective or Purpose

Hypothesis

Materials

Procedure

Data and Observations

DATA TABLE

Results

Discussion and Conclusions

SCIENTIFIC LAB REPORT
Experiment 6.4
A Model of Plate Tectonics

Objective or Purpose

Hypothesis

Materials

Procedure

Data and Observations

DATA TABLE

Results

Discussion and Conclusions

SCIENTIFIC LAB REPORT
Experiment 7.1
A Long-Term Weather Experiment

Objective or Purpose

Hypothesis

Materials

Procedure

Data table found on next two pages.

Results

Analyze your data using the questions found on page 198 in the text and write a paragraph to report any patterns you find.

Discussion and Conclusions

How can you use the weather patterns you determined to predict the weather in experiment 8.2?

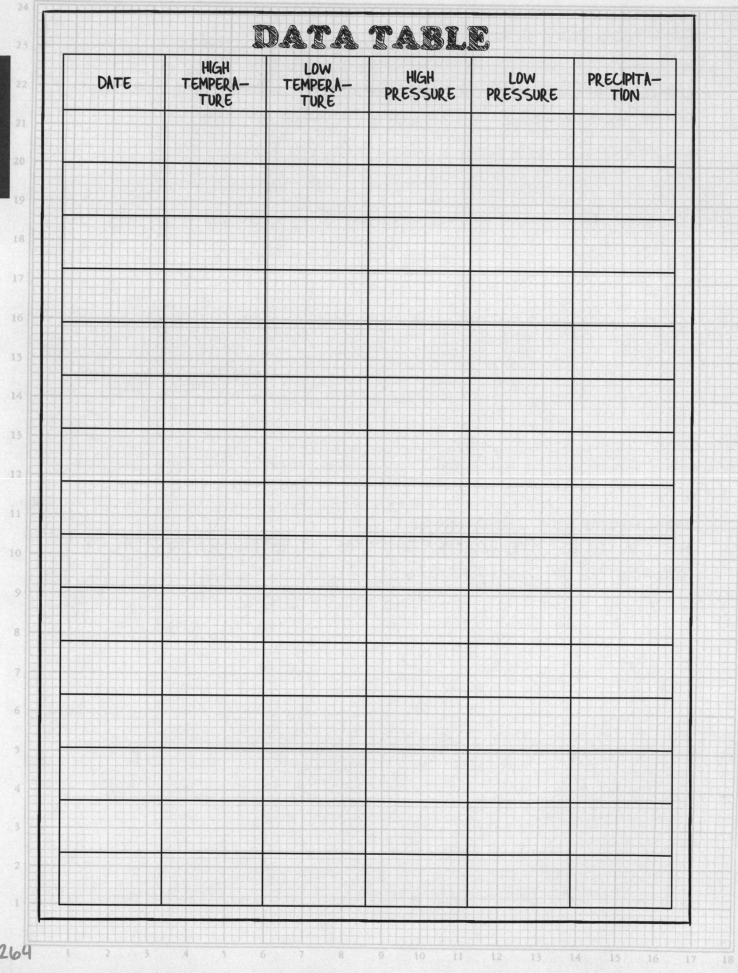

DATA TABLE

DATE	HIGH TEMPERA-TURE	LOW TEMPERA-TURE	HIGH PRESSURE	LOW PRESSURE	PRECIPITA-TION

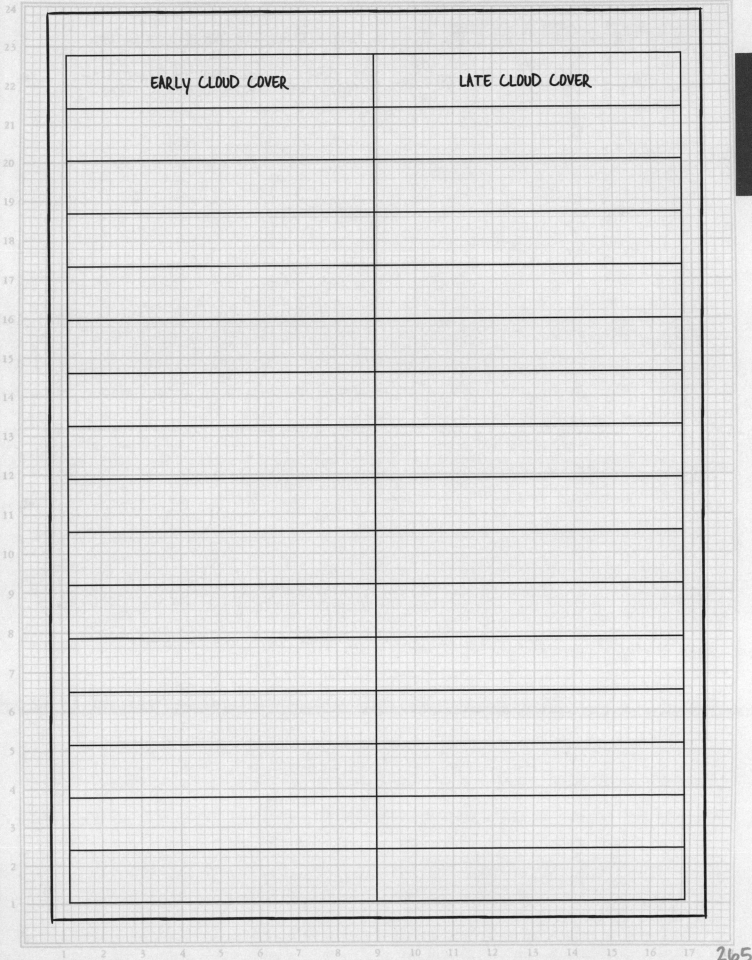

EARLY CLOUD COVER	LATE CLOUD COVER

DATA TABLE 2

AVAILABLE FOR FURTHER INVESTIGATION

DATE	HIGH TEMPERA-TURE	LOW TEMPERA-TURE	HIGH PRESSURE	LOW PRESSURE	PRECIPITA-TION

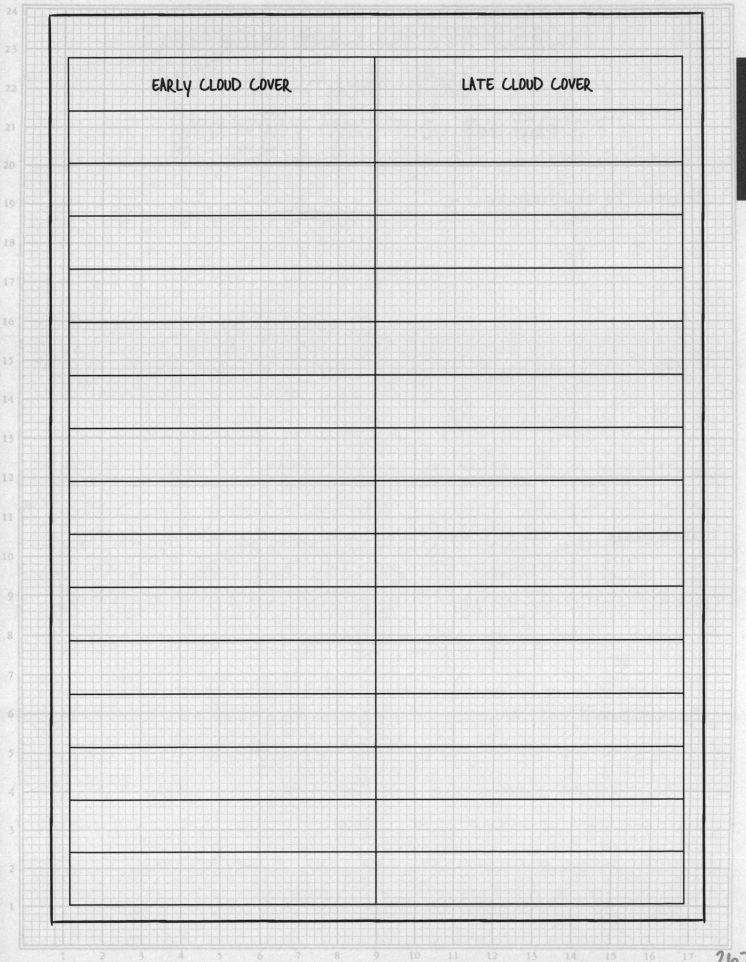

EARLY CLOUD COVER	LATE CLOUD COVER

SCIENTIFIC LAB REPORT
Experiment 8.1
Making your Own Lightning

Objective or Purpose

Hypothesis

Materials

Procedure

Data and Observations

DATA TABLE

Results

Discussion and Conclusions

SCIENTIFIC LAB REPORT
Experiment 8.2
Turning Experiment 7.1 into
a Weather Prediction Tool

Data and Observations

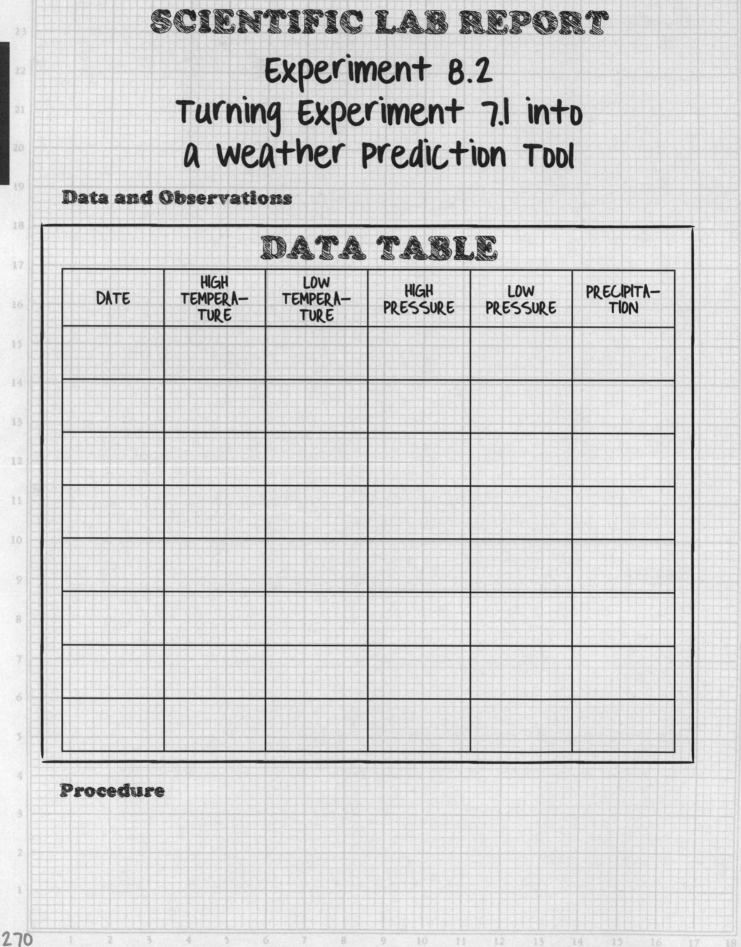

DATA TABLE

DATE	HIGH TEMPERA-TURE	LOW TEMPERA-TURE	HIGH PRESSURE	LOW PRESSURE	PRECIPITA-TION

Procedure

EARLY CLOUD COVER	LATE CLOUD COVER	YOUR PREDICTION	WEATHER FORECAST

Discussion and Conclusions

HOW CLOSE WERE YOUR PREDICTIONS TO THE WEATHER REPORTS AND TO THE ACTUAL WEATHER?

SCIENTIFIC LAB REPORT
Experiment 9.1
The Importance of Direction

Objective or Purpose

Hypothesis

Materials

Procedure

Data and Observations

DATA TABLE	
ONE EGG BEHIND THE OTHER	
ONE EGG AT THE BOTTOM	
ONE EGG ON EACH OF TWO RAMPS	

Results

Discussion and Conclusions

SCIENTIFIC LAB REPORT

Experiment 9.2
The Acceleration Due to Gravity Is
Independent of the Object Falling

Objective or Purpose

Hypothesis

Materials

Procedure

Data and Observations

<table>
<tr><td colspan="2" align="center">DATA TABLE</td></tr>
<tr><td>PAPER AND BOOK SEPARATELY</td><td></td></tr>
<tr><td>PAPER ON TOP OF BOOK</td><td></td></tr>
</table>

Results

Discussion and Conclusions

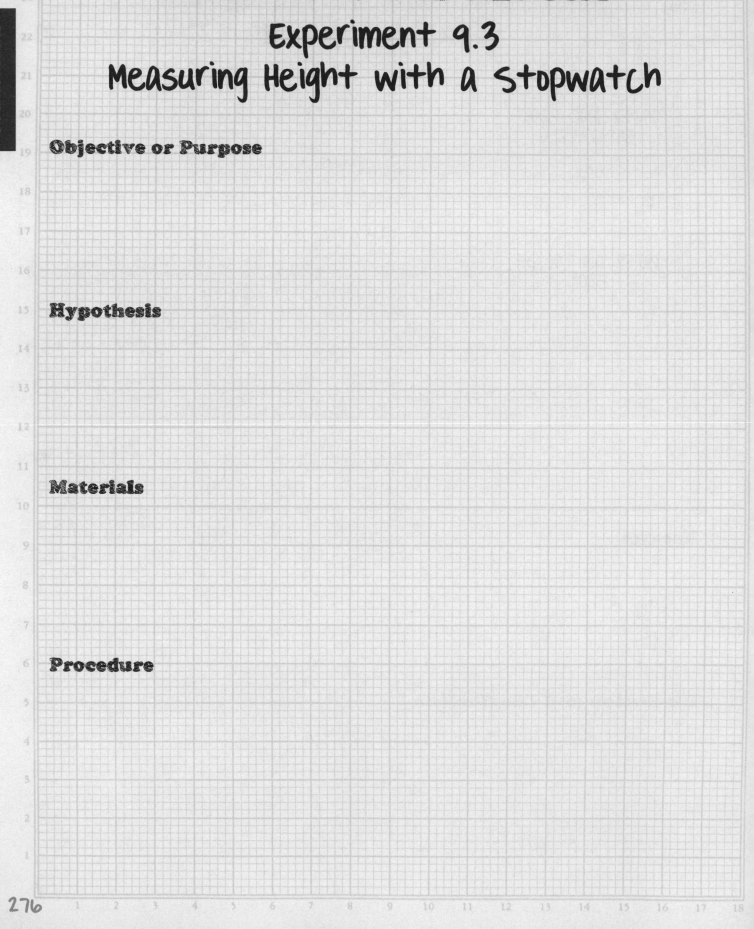

SCIENTIFIC LAB REPORT
Experiment 9.3
Measuring Height with a Stopwatch

Objective or Purpose

Hypothesis

Materials

Procedure

Data and Observations

DATA TABLE

TRIAL	TIME (SEC.)
1	
2	
3	
4	
5	
6	
7	
8	
9	
10	
Avg.	

Measured height of ceiling: _____

Calculations:

Comparison:

Results

Discussion and Conclusions

SCIENTIFIC LAB REPORT

Experiment 10.1
Two Experiments Demonstrating
Newton's First Law

Objective or Purpose

Hypothesis

Materials

Procedure

Data and Observations

DATA TABLE	
what happens to coin when flicking card quickly?	
what happens to coin when pulling card slowly?	
what happens when you spin the hard-boiled egg?	
what happens when you spin the raw egg?	
what happens when you spin, stop, let go of the hard-boiled egg?	
what happens when you spin, stop, let go of the raw egg?	

Results

Discussion and Conclusions

SCIENTIFIC LAB REPORT

Experiment 10.2
An Experiment to See How Well you understand Newton's First Law

Objective or Purpose

Hypothesis

Materials

Procedure

Data and Observations

DATA TABLE

Results

Discussion and Conclusions

SCIENTIFIC LAB REPORT
Experiment 10.3
Friction

Objective or Purpose

Hypothesis

Materials

Procedure

Data and Observations

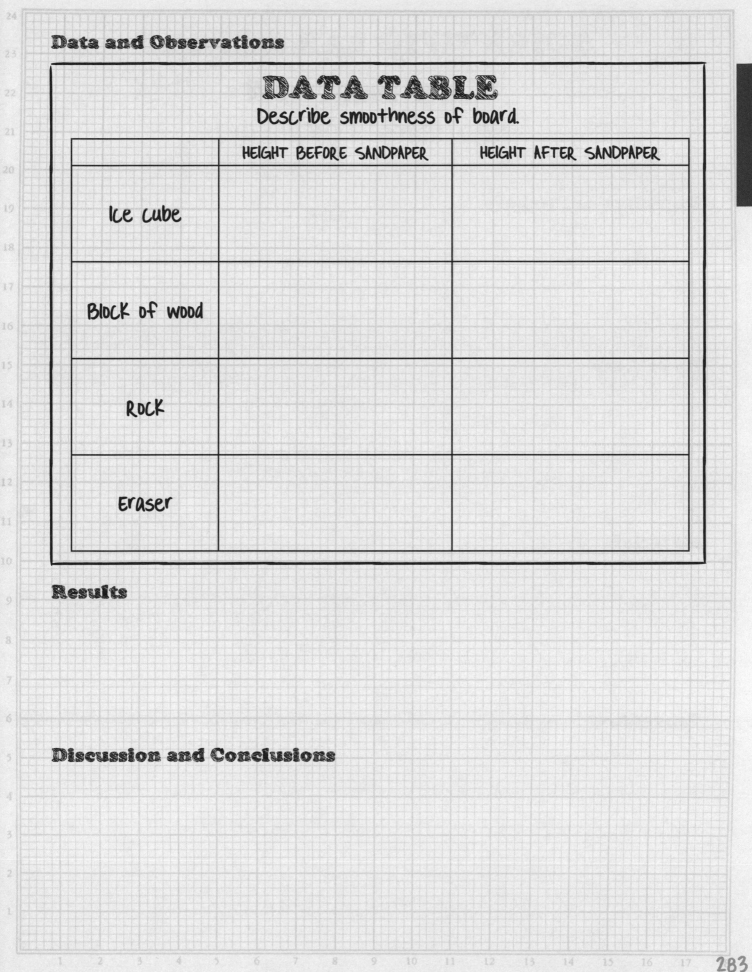

DATA TABLE
Describe smoothness of board.

	HEIGHT BEFORE SANDPAPER	HEIGHT AFTER SANDPAPER
Ice cube		
Block of wood		
Rock		
Eraser		

Results

Discussion and Conclusions

SCIENTIFIC LAB REPORT
Experiment 10.4
Newton's Third Law

Objective or Purpose

Hypothesis

Materials

Procedure

Data and Observations

+---+
| DATA TABLE |
| |
| |
| |
| |
| |
| |
| |
+---+

Results

Discussion and Conclusions

SCIENTIFIC LAB REPORT
Experiment 11.1
Force and Circular Motion

Objective or Purpose

Hypothesis

Materials

Procedure

Data and Observations

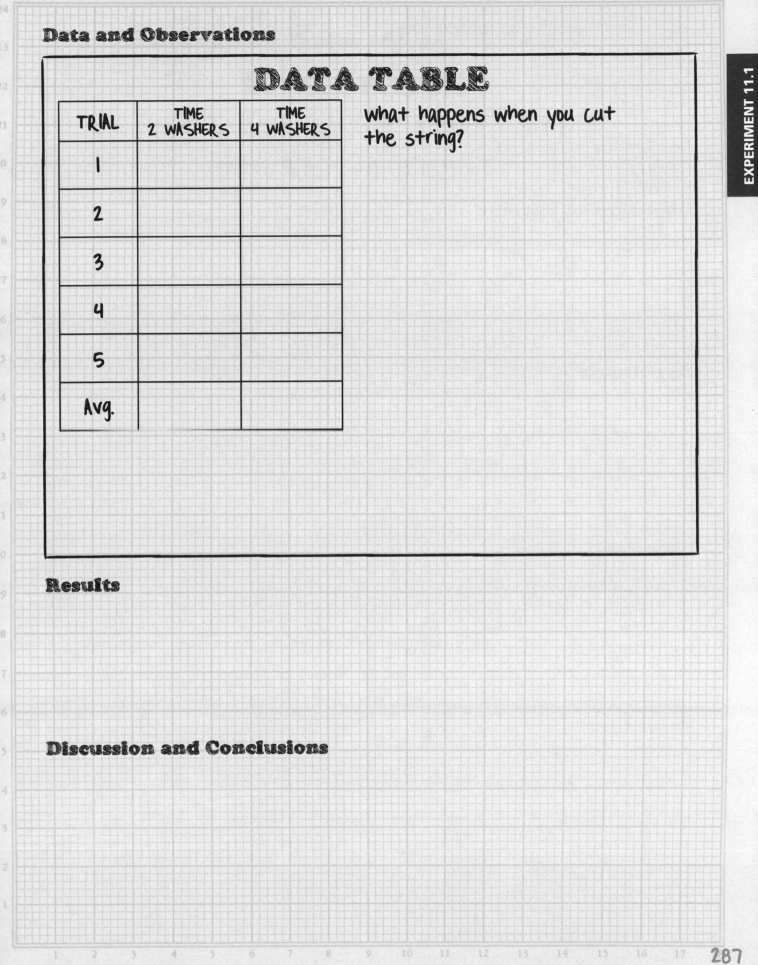

DATA TABLE

TRIAL	TIME 2 WASHERS	TIME 4 WASHERS
1		
2		
3		
4		
5		
Avg.		

what happens when you cut the string?

Results

Discussion and Conclusions

SCIENTIFIC LAB REPORT
Experiment 11.2
The "Bent Space and Time"
Theory of Gravity

Objective or Purpose

Hypothesis

Materials

Procedure

Data and Observations

DATA TABLE

	OBSERVATIONS
Marble when bowling ball is placed on cushion	
Path of marble with bowling ball removed	
Path of marble with bowling ball in middle	

Results

Discussion and Conclusions

SCIENTIFIC LAB REPORT
Experiment 11.3
The Graviton Theory of Gravity

Objective or Purpose

Hypothesis

Materials

Procedure

Data and Observations

DATA TABLE

	DESCRIBE DIFFICULTY
1 foot apart	
3 feet apart	
5 feet apart	
7 feet apart	
10 feet apart	

Results

Discussion and Conclusions

SCIENTIFIC LAB REPORT
Experiment 12.1
Electrical Attraction and Repulsion

Objective or Purpose

Hypothesis

Materials

Procedure

Data and Observations

DATA TABLE

	OBSERVATIONS
Balloon to balloon 1 (steps 5–6)	
Balloon to balloon 2 (steps 7–8)	
Tape to balloon 3 (steps 10–12)	

Results

Discussion and Conclusions

SCIENTIFIC LAB REPORT
Experiment 12.2
Making and Using an Electroscope

Objective or Purpose

Hypothesis

Materials

Procedure

Data and Observations

DATA TABLE	
	DESCRIBE MOTION OF THE FOIL STRIPS
Balloon to loop without touching (step 9)	
Balloon touches paper clip (step 10)	
Pull balloon away (step 11)	
Touch loop with finger (step 12)	
Steps 13–16	

Results

Discussion and Conclusions

SCIENTIFIC LAB REPORT
Experiment 12.3
Current and Resistance

Objective or Purpose

Hypothesis

Materials

Procedure

Data and Observations

DATA TABLE

Results

Discussion and Conclusions

SCIENTIFIC LAB REPORT

Experiment 14.1
The Medium through which
Sound Waves Travel

Objective or Purpose

Hypothesis

Materials

Procedure

Data and Observations

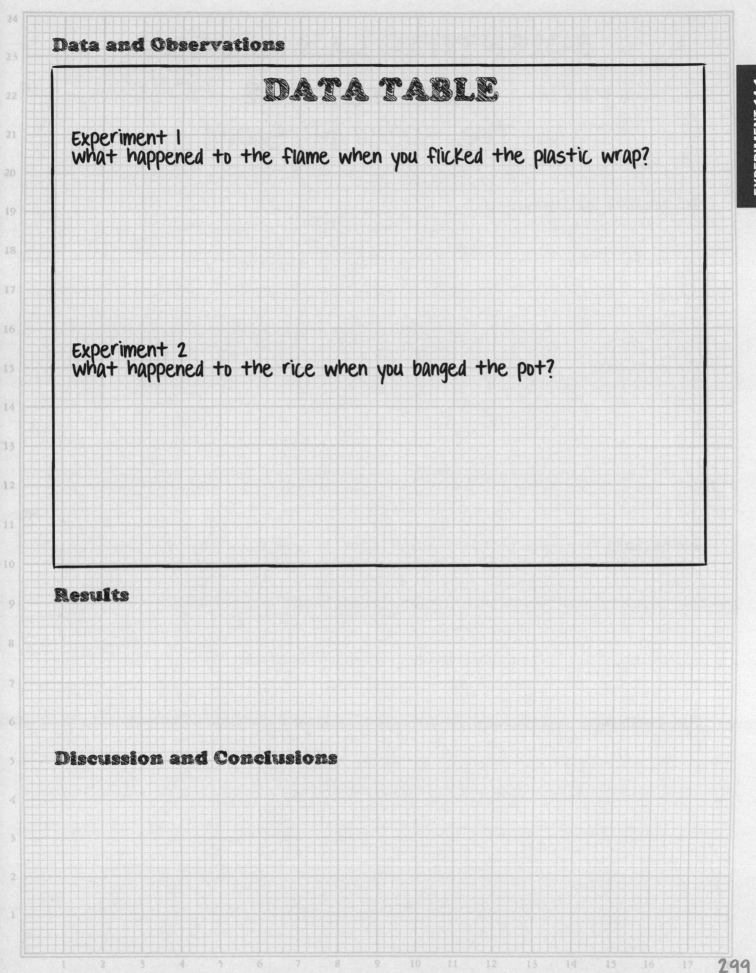

DATA TABLE

Experiment 1
What happened to the flame when you flicked the plastic wrap?

Experiment 2
What happened to the rice when you banged the pot?

Results

Discussion and Conclusions

SCIENTIFIC LAB REPORT
Experiment 14.2
The Speed of Sound

Objective or Purpose

Hypothesis

Materials

Procedure

Data and Observations

DATA TABLE

TRIAL	DISTANCE (METERS)
1	
2	
3	
Avg.	

TRIAL	TIME (SEC.)
1	
2	
3	
4	
5	
6	
7	
8	
9	
10	
Avg.	

Calculations:

Results

Discussion and Conclusions

SCIENTIFIC LAB REPORT
Experiment 14.3
Wavelength and Sound

Objective or Purpose

Hypothesis

Materials

Procedure

Data and Observations

DATA TABLE

TRIAL	DESCRIBE THE DIFFERENCE IN SOUND
Empty to 3/4 full	
3/4 to 1/2 full	
1/2 to 1/4 full	
Empty	

Results

Discussion and Conclusions

SCIENTIFIC LAB REPORT
Experiment 14.4
The Doppler Effect

Objective or Purpose

Hypothesis

Materials

Procedure

Data and Observations

```
                        DATA TABLE

   Describe the difference in the sound of the horn before the car
   passes and after.




   How does the sound of the stopped car's horn compare?
```

Results

Discussion and Conclusions

SCIENTIFIC LAB REPORT
Experiment 14.5
The Amplitude of a Sound wave

Objective or Purpose

Hypothesis

Materials

Procedure

DATA TABLE

Describe how the sound and the vibrations change the harder you pluck.

Results

Discussion and Conclusions

SCIENTIFIC LAB REPORT
Experiment 15.1
Seeing Different Wavelengths of Light

Objective or Purpose

Hypothesis

Materials

Procedure

Data and Observations

DATA TABLE

Draw the rainbow you made.

Results

Discussion and Conclusions

SCIENTIFIC LAB REPORT
Experiment 15.2
The Law of Reflection

Objective or Purpose

Hypothesis

Materials

Procedure

Data and Observations

DATA TABLE

Draw the angles you saw.

Results

Discussion and Conclusions

SCIENTIFIC LAB REPORT
Experiment 15.3
Refraction of Light

Objective or Purpose

Hypothesis

Materials

Procedure

Data and Observations

DATA TABLE

Explain what happens to the light beam.

Results

Discussion and Conclusions

SCIENTIFIC LAB REPORT
Experiment 15.4
The "Magical" Quarter

Objective or Purpose

Hypothesis

Materials

Procedure

Data and Observations

DATA TABLE

Results

Discussion and Conclusions

SCIENTIFIC LAB REPORT
Experiment 15.5
How the Eye Detects Color

Objective or Purpose

Hypothesis

Materials

Procedure

Data and Observations

DATA TABLE

Draw what you saw.

Results

Discussion and Conclusions

SCIENTIFIC LAB REPORT

Experiment 16.1
An Expanding universe

Objective or Purpose

Hypothesis

Materials

Procedure

DATA TABLE

How do the dots move in relation to one another?

Results

Discussion and Conclusions

Summaries

These fill-in-the-blank summaries are strictly optional. They are provided for extra practice for students who are having trouble studying for the module tests. If you have mastered the material for a module, your parent may have you skip the summary and take the test after you have reviewed your notes on the text.

MODULE 1 SUMMARY (OPTIONAL)

1 Atoms are the ___Smallest chemical___ unit of matter. They are so

___small___ that you cannot see them. Images of atoms produced

by scanning tunneling electron microscopes are not pictures, but are the result of

computer ___calculations___. Such images are part of the large amount of

___indirect___ evidence that indicates atoms exist. When two or more

atoms link together, they form a ___molecule___, which has its own unique

properties.

2 When a substance is made of billions and billions of the same atom, it is called an

___Element___, while substances made up of billions and billions of

the same molecule are called ___Compounds___. Some substances, called

___mixturse___, are made of more than one kind of atom or molecule. In

experiment 1.1, you watched the molecule known as ___Water molecule___ break

down into two elements: ___hydrogen___ and ___oxygen___.

In addition, you saw the ___copper___ in the wire (an element) react with

___backing soda___ molecules to make copper hydroxycarbonate.

3 When making measurements, the ___Unit___ we report are just as

important as the numbers. The base metric unit for mass is the ___gram___,

while the base English unit for mass is the ___slug___. The base metric

unit for weight is the ___Newton___, while the base English unit for weight is

the ___Pound___. Although the weight of an object varies depending on

gravity, the ___mass___ does not.

4 The base metric unit for length is the ___meter___ , and the base

English unit for length is the ___foot___ . The base metric unit for

volume is the ___liter___ , and the base English unit for volume is the

___gallon___ .

5 In the metric system, prefixes govern the ___size___ of a unit. The "milli"

prefix means ___0.001___ , while the ___centi___ prefix

means 0.01. The "kilo" prefix means ___1,000___ . Thus, an object with a

mass of 1 centigram has ___less___ mass than an object with a mass of 1

kilogram.

6 The metric unit for temperature is degrees ___Celsius___ . This unit uses

no prefixes. In this system, water freezes at ___0 degrees Celcius___ and boils at

___100 degrees Celcius___

7 In the Old Testament, a measurement unit for length called the ___cubit___

was used.

8 Concentration is the ___quantity___ of a substance within a

certain ___volume___ . At certain concentrations, chemicals behave

___in one way___ . At other concentrations, those same chemicals can behave

___in a different way___ . Vitamins, for example, are ___good___ for your body at low

concentrations, but they become ___toxic___ at high concentrations. In experiment 1.3,

the more concentrated the vinegar, the ___faster___ the antacid tablet disappeared.

9 In this course, we do conversions using the _____facter-label_____ method, in which the measurement you want to convert is multiplied by a fraction that contains both the original unit and the unit you want to convert to.

Solve the Following Problems

10 Convert 34.5 kL into L.

$$1 KL = 1000 L \text{ or. } 1 L = 0.001 KL$$

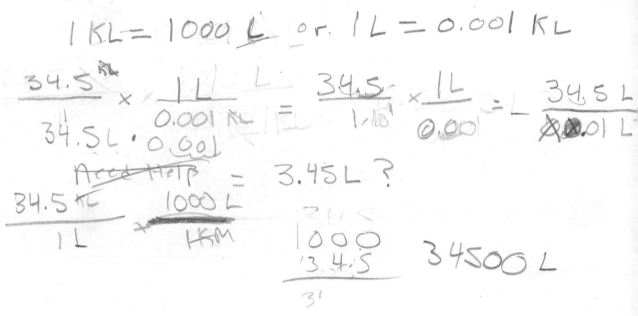

$$\frac{34.5}{34.5 L} \times \frac{1 L}{0.001 KL} = \frac{34.5}{1.00} \times \frac{1 L}{0.00} = \frac{34.5 L}{0.01 L}$$

$$34.5 L \cdot 0.001$$

Acce Help = 3.45 L ?

$$\frac{34.5 KL}{1 L} \times \frac{1000 L}{1 KM}$$

$$\begin{array}{r} 1000 \\ 3.4.5 \\ \hline 31 \end{array} \quad 34500 L$$

11 Convert 0.00045 g to mg.

$$1 g = 1000 mg$$

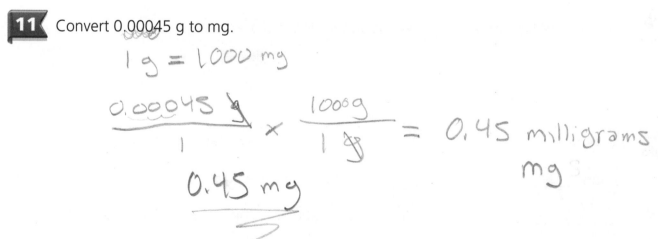

$$\frac{0.00045 \cancel{g}}{1} \times \frac{1000 g}{1 \cancel{g}} = 0.45 \text{ milligrams}$$
$$mg$$

$$\underline{0.45 \, mg}$$

12 Which takes up more volume: 45 mL or 0.6 L?

$1 mL = 0.001 L$

$45 mL \times \dfrac{1 L}{1000 mL} =$

$0.6 L$

45.000

$\boxed{45000 L}$

$1 mL = 0.001 L$

$1 L = 1000 mL$

$= 0.045 L$

$45 \cdot 0.001$

$.045 \cdot 10^{-3}$

$\underline{0.045 L}$

13 How many centigrams are in 13.1 g?

$100 cg = 1 g$

$13.1 \cdot 100 = 131 cg$ are in a gram

14 If an object has a volume of 45.1 mL, what is its volume in liters?

$1 L = 1000 mL$

$1 mL = 0.001 L$

$45.1 \cdot 0.001$

$45.1 \cdot 1000 ?$

$451 L ?$

15 If a road is 13.1 miles long, how many feet long is it? (1 mile = 5,280 feet)

$$13.1 \frac{m}{1} \times \frac{5280 \, F}{1 \, m} \qquad 13.1 \times 5280$$

16 How many cm are in 16.2 m?

100 cm = 1 m

$16.2 \cdot 100 = 1620 \, cm = 16.2 \, m$

17 If an object has a mass of 345.6 mg, what is its mass in grams?

$$\frac{34.6 \, mg}{1} \times \frac{1 \, gm}{1000 \, mg} \qquad 34.6 \cdot 1000 \qquad 1 \, mg = 0.001 \, gm$$

$$1 \, gm = 1000 \, mg$$

34,600 g

$$\frac{34.6 \quad 0.001 \, gm}{1 \quad 1 \, mg}$$

$0.0346 \, g = 345.6 \, mg$

0.0346 g

18 If a football field is 100.0 yards long, how many feet long is it? (1 yard = 3 feet)

$$\frac{100.0\ \cancel{yd}}{1} \times \frac{3\ ft}{1\ \cancel{yd}} = 100.0 \times 3 = \boxed{300\ ft}$$

19 Convert 451 grams into kg.

$$\frac{451\ g}{1} \times \frac{1\ kg}{1000\ \cancel{g}} \qquad 451 \times 0.001\ kg = 0.451\ kg$$

$$451\ g = 0.451\ kg$$

MODULE 2 SUMMARY (OPTIONAL)

1 The moisture content of air is called ___humidity___ . God has designed you to ___Sweat___ when you are too warm. This releases water onto your skin, ___nothing goes here___ which then evaporates. The process of evaporation requires ___energy___ , which is supplied by your skin. As a result, when your sweat evaporates, the net effect is that your skin ___cools___ . When the humidity is high, your sweat does not ___evaporate___ as quickly, and as a result, you do not cool down as well. For this reason, many weather reports include a ___Heat Index___ , which is a combination of temperature and humidity.

2 There are two ways of reporting humidity: ___absolute___ and ___relative___ . If you report the mass of water vapor contained in a certain volume of air, you are reporting the ___absolute Humidity___ . If you report the ratio of the mass of water vapor in the air at a given temperature to the maximum mass of water vapor the air could hold at that temperature, you are reporting the ___relative Humidity___ .

3 On a day when the relative humidity is high, water evaporates ___slowly___ . On a day when the relative humidity is low, water evaporates more ___quickly___ . If the relative humidity is ___100%___ , we say that the air is saturated with water.

4 Dry air (air that has all of the _water vapor_ removed) is 78% _nitrogen_, _21%_ oxygen, and 1% _other gases_. This is an _ideal_ mixture of gases to support life. The oxygen is necessary in order to allow our bodies to run _combustion_ reactions. Without enough oxygen, our bodies would run out of the _energy_ necessary for life. Too much oxygen in the atmosphere, however, can cause _health_ problems in people and significantly increase the number of natural _forest fires_.

5 The majority of the air we breathe in is nitrogen, and the majority of the air that we breathe out is _nitrogen_. In addition to nitrogen, the other major gases we exhale are _oxygen_, _water vaper_, and _carbon dioxide_. Of those three gases, we exhale significantly more _oxygen_ than the other two. _carbon dioxide_ enters the atmosphere as a result of organisms breathing and as the result of fires.

6 Through a process called photosynthesis, plants convert _carbon dioxide_ and water into glucose, which they use for food. A byproduct of this process is _oxygen_. In addition to allowing plants to manufacture their own food, _the greenhouse effect_ helps regulate the temperature of the earth. Through a process referred to as the _greenhouse effect_, this gas traps heat that radiates from the earth. Without such gases, the average temperature of the earth would be far too _low_ to support life.

7   If the greenhouse effect ran out of control, we would have _global warming_, a

situation in which the average temperature of the earth increased over time. Although

this would be bad, the greenhouse effect is _necessary_, as it makes

life on Earth possible. Since carbon dioxide is a gas that participates in the greenhouse

effect, the fact that the concentration of carbon dioxide in the atmosphere is

rising makes some people fear that _global warming_

may already be happening.

8   The average temperature of the earth has changed _little_ in the

past 100 years. There was a small _increase_ in the average global

temperature from the late 1800s to the early 1900s, but that was before carbon dioxide

levels in ___ the atmosphere _increased_

they want me to say (little) but I will

say

significantly. Thus, there is _lots of_ evidence that increasing carbon

dioxide concentration causes _global warming_. In addition, the earth was

significantly _warmer_ between the ninth and fourteenth centuries

than it is today.

9   Ultraviolet light is _harmful_ to living organisms because it has enough

energy to _distroy / kill_ living tissue. Although the sun produces a

significant amount of ultraviolet light, most of it is blocked by _ozone_

in the _ozone_ layer. This gas is _toxic_, but

the _ozone_ layer is high above sea level, where no one is breathing.

Even though most ultraviolet light from the sun is blocked, some gets through, and if your

skin is exposed to too much of it, you can get a _sun burn_.

10 When we report concentration in parts per million, we are reporting the number of molecules (or atoms) of a substance in a mixture for every 1 _million_ molecules (or atoms) in the mixture. The concentration of many pollutants is often expressed in parts per million, as their concentrations are very _low_. Despite what many people think, the concentrations of pollutants in Earth's atmosphere have been _decreasing_ for some time. Thus, the air we are breathing today is _cleaner_ than it was 30 years ago.

11 Sulfur oxides are put in the atmosphere when sulfur _burns_. Sulfur is a _contaminate_ in all _fuels_ we burn. The sulfur content of coal can be _reduced_ in a process called "cleaning." Many industries have devices in their _smookstacks_ that help clean the sulfur oxides out of the mixture of gases that result from burning fuel. These devices are commonly called _scrubbers_. Although human activity puts sulfur oxides in the atmosphere, there are natural sources as well, one of the most important being _volcanes_.

12 Nitrogen oxides are formed when _Nitrogen_ burns. This happens at very high _temperatures_, so engines and power plants are major human-made sources of nitrogen oxides. There are, however, many natural sources of nitrogen oxides as well, such as _volcanes_, _lightning_, and _biological decay_.

13 While ozone in the ozone layer protects living organisms, ozone is a _Toxic gas_ . Thus, _ground_ -level ozone is a pollutant because people breathe it. Ozone in the _Ozone layer_ is not a pollutant, however, because no one can breathe it.

14 _Carbon monoxide_ is a toxic byproduct of incomplete combustion. Unlike carbon dioxide, this gas can be _deadly_ , even at concentrations as low as a few hundred parts per million. Automobiles used to be a major source of this gas, but the introduction of _Catalytic converters_ significantly reduced the amount produced in automobiles by converting the gas into _Carbon dioxide_ .

15 The U.S. government began issuing standards called _CAFE Standard_ , which regulate the average number of miles an automobile can travel on a single gallon of gasoline. Although these standards do _Reduce_ automobile-related pollution, they also _Increase_ the number of traffic fatalities.

16 When one compares the positive result of an action to the negative result and decides whether or not the positive result was worth the accompanying negative result, we say that the person has done a _Cost/ benefit_ . Any reasonable discussion of air pollution _regulations_ must include such an analysis in order to ensure that the reduced pollution is worth whatever accompanying costs exist.

$$1\% = 10,000 \text{ ppm}$$

Solve the Following Problems

17 The concentration of a pollutant in a sample of air is about 0.03%. What is this in ppm?

$$\frac{0.03\%}{1} \cdot \frac{10,000\ ppm}{1\%} \qquad \boxed{300\ ppm}$$

18 Convert 151 ppm into percent.

$$\frac{151\ ppm}{1} \qquad \frac{1\%}{10,000\ ppm} \qquad \frac{151\%}{10000} \qquad \boxed{0.0151\%}$$

19 The current concentration of a gas in an air sample is 0.091 ppm. What is that in percent?

$$\frac{0000.091\ ppm}{1} \qquad \frac{1\%}{10,000\ ppm}$$

$$\frac{0000.091}{10000} \qquad \% = 0.0000091\%$$

20 Suppose you had a sample of air in which the sulfur oxides concentration is 0.011%.

What would the concentration of sulfur oxides be if you expressed it in ppm?

$$\frac{0.011\%}{1} \quad \frac{10,000 \text{ ppm}}{1\%}$$

110 ppm

MODULE 3 SUMMARY (OPTIONAL)

1 The mass of air surrounding a planet is called its _Atmosphere_ . Everything that comes into contact with the mass of air surrounding Earth is subjected to _Atmospheric pressure_ , which is, on average, 14.7 pounds per square inch at sea level. Even though this is a lot of pressure, we don't feel it, because _equal_ pressure pushes on you from all sides, even from within.

2 In experiment 3.1, the cans were filled with steam that turned into _liquid water_ when the cans were put in ice water. The upright can did not crumple, however, because the steam was replaced with _air_ that continued to exert _Pressure_ on the inside of the can. The can placed _upside down_ in the water did crumple, however, because _air_ could not replace the steam, so very little _Pressure_ was being exerted inside the can.

3 A _barometer_ measures atmospheric pressure. It is composed of a tube with no _Air_ inside that is inverted over a pool of _liquid_ , which is usually mercury. Since the _Atmosphere_ is pressing down on the pool, and since there is no air exerting _Pressure_ inside the tube, _liquid_ is forced up the tube. The _height_ of the liquid in the tube is a measure of the _Atmospheric Pressure_ .

4 When measuring atmospheric pressure, several units can be used. _Pounds per square Inch_ tells you how many pounds are exerted on a ~~X~~ 1-inch by 1-inch square. When reported in ___Inches___ , it tells you the height of a column of mercury in a barometer in English units. When reported in ___mmHg___ , it tells you the height of the column of mercury in metric units. Finally, pressure can also be reported in ___Atmosphere or Atm___ , which tells you the pressure relative to Earth's average atmospheric pressure at sea level.

5 The atmosphere can be divided into two general layers. The ___homosphere___ is the lower layer, and it contains air that has the same ___composistion___ as the air at sea level. The upper layer is called the ___heterosphere___ , and the mixture of gases in this layer is not ___Perfect or uniform___ . Throughout both layers, however, the total amount of air ___decreases___ with increasing altitude.

6 The homosphere is generally divided into three regions. From lowest to highest, they are the ___troposphere___ , the ___stratosphere___ , and the ___mesosphere___ . The first two layers are separated by the ___tropopause___ , the second two are separated by the ___stratopause___ , and the last layer is separated from the heterosphere by the ___mesopause___ . Throughout all of these regions, as well as the heterosphere, the atmospheric pressure continually ___changes decreases___ with increasing altitude.

7 In the troposphere, the temperature steadily ___decreases___ with increasing altitude. This is called the temperature ___gratient___ of the troposphere. The troposphere is often called Earth's ___weather___ layer because it

336

MODULE 3

contains almost all of Earth's clouds, rain, snow, storms, etc.

8 Narrow bands of high-speed winds that circle the earth, blowing from west to east, are called ___Jet Streams___ . They are found in the ___lower___ portions of the stratosphere and the ___upper___ portions of the troposphere. They tend to ___Steer?___ storms and affect which parts of the earth experience high ___atmospheric___ or low ___atmospheric___ .

9 In the stratosphere, the temperature ___increases___ with increasing altitude. This is mostly due to the ___(ozone layer)²___ , which is found there. In the mesosphere, the temperature ___decreases___ with increasing altitude. When rocks from outer space fall into the mesosphere and burn up, they are called ___Meteors___ .

2. we have not learned that yet

10 When energy is transferred as a consequence of temperature differences, we call it ___heat___ . When an object gains energy, the ___Molecules (or Atoms)___ that make it up move faster. A ___thermometer___ really measures the average speed at which the ___Molecules (Atoms)___ of a substance are moving. As a result, temperature is a measure of the ___energy___ of ___random motion___ in a substance's ___Molecules (Atoms)___

11 The "hole" in the ozone layer is actually a seasonal ___decrease___ in the concentration of ozone in the ozone layer. It is centered over ___Antarctica___ . Human-made substances called ___CFCs___ are at least partially to blame. Unlike many chemicals, they are so ___unreactive___ ~~harmless~~ that they can survive the trip up to the ozone layer, where they can destroy ozone. Interestingly enough, this same property makes them ___harmless___ to human beings. They are very efficient chemicals that can be used for ___surgical sterilizes___ ___firefighting___, and ___refrigeration___ . Despite their usefulness, their elimination has been called for by the ___Montreal Protocol___. This will, most likely, cause an ___increase___ in the number of people who die each year.

12 The "hole" in the ozone layer was discovered ___long before___ CFCs were widely used. However, since the production of CFCs, the "hole" has gotten

" ___deeper___ ." Although CFCs are heavy, they are lifted up to the ozone layer by the ___polar vortex___ . This is why the ozone "hole" is a ___seasonal___ phenomenon and why it is centered over ___Antartica___ . While the elimination of CFCs will ___reduce___ the depth of the ozone "hole," it will most likely ___lost___ more lives than it will save. The ozone "hole" does *not* contribute to ___global warming___ . In fact, a reduction in the amount of ozone in the ozone layer will ___cool___ the average temperature of the earth.

13 The heterosphere is generally divided into two layers: the ___thermosphere___ and the ___exosphere___ . While the ___thermosphere___ is lower than the ___exosphere___ , they can both be considered a part of outer space. The number of molecules in the ___thermosphere___ is so small that a thermometer would read incredibly low temperatures. However, the average ___energy___ of the few molecules that are there is very _____high_____ . The _____exosphere_____ is composed of those

atoms and molecules actually in orbit around the _____earth_____ . It is

difficult to say where the _____exosphere_____ ends and interplanetary space

begins.

14 Between the upper portions of the _____mesosphere_____ and the lower portions

of the _____thermosphere_____ , there is a region where the atmosphere's gases are

ionized. It is called the _____ionosphere_____ . Atoms are composed of

_____electrons_____ (which have positive electrical charge),

_____nuetrons_____ (which have negative electrical charge), and

_____protons_____ (which have no electrical charge). Atoms always have the

same number of _____nuetrons_____ and _____electrons_____ . This

means that overall, atoms have no net _____electrical charge_____ . When an atom

loses (or gains) electrons, there is an _____inbulance_____ of positive and negative

charges, and the atom becomes _____electricly charged_____ -7(ionized). When this happens, it is no

longer an atom, but is instead an _____ion_____ .

15 The Northern Lights and Southern Lights are examples of _____Auroras_____ .

They appear in the night sky as glowing regions of brilliant _____light_____

that tend to move over the sky in interesting ways. They are the result of high-energy

_____collisions_____ between ionized particles in the _____ionosphere_____ .

MODULE 4 SUMMARY (OPTIONAL)

1 We can live for as many as two weeks without food, but if we were to go even a few days without _____Water_____ , we would surely die. Indeed, without water, _____life_____ as we know it simply cannot exist.

2 The use of electricity to break a molecule down into smaller units is called _____electrolysis_____ . When you use this procedure on water, you produce _____Oxygen_____ and _____hydrogen_____ . If you measure the volumes of each, you will find twice as much _____hydrogen_____ as _____Oxygen_____ .

3 Often, experiments produce incorrect results due to _____experimental error_____. A good scientist tries to _____reduce_____ the amount of it in an experiment and does not _____trust_____ experiments that have a lot of it. When a scientist performs an experiment that seems to lead to a new, interesting conclusion, other _____Scientists_____ in the field look closely at the experiment in an effort to spot _____experimental error_____ that the original scientist did not recognize. This process is called _____Peer veiw_____ . An example of the importance of this process is seen in Drs. Martin Fleischmann and Stanley Pons, who claimed to have discovered _____Cold fusion_____ , a potential source of cheap, unlimited power. They did not submit their experiments to _____Peer view_____ before publicizing their results. As a result, they were embarrassed because other scientists had to publicly announce the _____experimental error_____ in their experiments.

4 The chemical symbol of an atom contains either _one_ or _two_ letters. If there are _two_ letters, only the _first_ ~~e~~ is capitalized. The letters often come from either the _English_ or _Latin_ name of the atom. A _Chemical formula_ tells you the composition of a molecule because the _Subscripts_ in the chemical formula tell you how many of each atom is present. If there is no subscript next to an atom's symbol, there is _one_ of those atoms in the molecule. Thus, the molecule $CaCO_3$ has _one_ calcium (Ca) atom, _one_ carbon (C) atom, and _three_ oxygen (O) atoms.

5 Magnesium hydroxide is a chemical often used in antacid tablets. It has one Magnesium (Mg) atom, two oxygen (O) atoms, and two hydrogen (H) atoms. Thus, its chemical formula is _MgO_2H_2_ . The chemical formula of sodium nitrate is $NaNO_3$. This molecule has a total of _five_ atoms: _one_ sodium (Na) atom, _one_ nitrogen (N) atom, and _three_ oxygen (O) atoms.

6 Atoms in molecules are linked together with _Chemical bond_ , which are made up of _Shared_ electrons. If the atoms in a molecule do not _Share_ electrons equally, small _~~ul~~ Charges_ result within the molecule, and it is called a _Polar_ molecule. In experiment 4.2, the small _Positive_ charges on the _hydrogen_ atoms of the water molecules were attracted to the _Negative_ charge on the comb. That's what made the stream of water bend _towards_ the comb. When you dissolve a substance in a liquid, we say you have made a

7 ___Solution___ . When making a solution, you use a

___solvent___ to dissolve a ___solute___ . When you dissolve

sugar in water, for example, water is the ___solvent___ , sugar is the

___solute___ , and sugar water is the ___solution___ .

8 In general, a polar or ionic solute can only dissolve in a ___Polar/Ionic___

solvent. A nonpolar solute can only dissolve in a ___nonpolar___ solvent. A

solute dissolves in a solvent because the molecules of the solvent are

___attracted___ to the molecules (or ions) of the solute.

9 In a water molecule, the positive charge on one molecule is attracted to any other

___Negative___ charge. In a sample of water, there are many other

molecules, so they will tend to align themselves so that the positive charge on the

___hydrogen Atom___ of one molecule will be as close as possible to the

negative charge on the ___Oxygen Atom___ of another molecule. This results in

___hydrogen bonding___ , which causes water molecules to be very close to one

another. In fact, most molecules that are chemically similar to water are

___gases___ at room temperature. Water, however, is a

___liquid___ at room temperature because of ___hydrogen bonding___

10 While the solid phase of most substances ___sinks___ in the liquid phase

of that same substance, solid water (ice) ___floats___ in liquid water.

This is because the molecules of liquid water are ___closer together___ than the

molecules in solid water. This convenient fact allows lakes to ___freeze___

342

from the top down. As a result, a reasonably deep body of water will never

_____completely_____ freeze because the _____Ice_____ at the

surface insulates the water below. This allows fish (and other aquatic animals) to

_____Survive_____ the winter.

11 Because of hydrogen bonding, individual water molecules are so strongly

_____attracted_____ to one another that they tend to stay together, even when

subjected to an outside force. This gives water its _____Cohesion_____ , which,

in turn, causes _____Surface tension_____, the phenomenon that caused the needle to

float in experiment 4.5. This same phenomenon is exploited by water striders, allowing

them to _____walk_____ on water. The _____Cohesion_____ of water

is also what makes it possible for water to travel up through the xylem of a tall plant.

12 Although water's _____Cohesion_____ is strong, it can be overcome. In experiment

4.6, for example, water "beaded up" on the _____waxed_____ surface of

the glass because water molecules are attracted to _____each other_____ more

_____strongly_____ than they are to molecules that make up wax. However, the

water did not "bead up" on the unwaxed glass because water molecules are attracted to

_____The molecules that make up glass_____ more _____Strongly_____

than they are to each other.

13 When water has ions like calcium and magnesium dissolved in it, we call it

_____hard_____ water. It is _____not_____ the result of treatment

done to make the water safe to drink. Instead, it is the result of the _____Source_____ from which the water is taken. In a _Water Softener_, calcium and magnesium ions are "exchanged" with either _Sodium_ or _Potassium_ ions so that the calcium and magnesium ions are not in the water we drink and use. People who are on strict _Sodium_ diets should either not soften their water or use more expensive, sodium-free water-softener salts, like _Potassium Chloride_.

MODULE 5 SUMMARY (OPTIONAL)

1 Water is such a large part of the earth that astronomers often call it the
Blue Planet planet. The sum of all water on a planet is called its
Hydrosphere . Of all the planets in our solar system, Earth is the
only planet that has a large quantity of water in its liquid form. This is
because Earth has _____ in its
atmosphere and is _Perfect distance_ from the sun.

2 The vast majority of Earth's water supply is contained in the _Ocean_
as _Saltwater_ . The vast majority of Earth's freshwater supply is stored
in _Glaciers_ and _Icebergs_ . The largest source of
liquid freshwater is _Groundwater_ . Aside from the sources just mentioned,
the other major sources of water in the hydrosphere are _Surface water_ (not
oceans), _Soil moister_ , and _Atmospheric moister_

3 The process by which water is continuously exchanged between the earth's various
water sources is called the _hydrolic cycle_ . In this process, water gets into
the atmosphere predominantly by _evaperation_ and
Transpiration . Soil moisture is usually depleted by either
Transpiration or _Groundwater flow_. Water vapor in the
atmosphere can form a cloud through a process called ~~water~~ _Condension_ . Once
water is in a cloud, it can fall back to the earth as _Presipitation_ . When this
water falls on land and then runs along the surface into a lake, river, or stream, we call it
Surface runoff .

4 Evaporation and condensation of a mixture to separate out the mixture's individual components is called _Distillation_ . This process is why water from the ocean can eventually end up in a _Freshwater_ source, like a lake, river, or stream.

5 The average time a given particle will stay in a given system is called its _Residence Time_ , and in the hydrologic cycle, it varies considerably from source to source. The average time a molecule of water stays in a swiftly flowing river, for example, is _2 weeks_ than that of a water molecule in a lake. The average time a molecule of water stays in the atmosphere is much _less_ than that of a water molecule in the ocean. The _Bible ?_ was the first work to mention the hydrologic cycle.

6 The chemical name of the salt you put on your food is _Sodium Chloride_ . Although this is the majority of salt in the ocean, chemists use the term "salt" more _Scientificly ?_ , and as a result, there are other salts in the ocean. A measure of the mass of dissolved salt in a given mass of water is called _Salinity_ .

7 Salt is found in the ocean because the only way water can escape the ocean is through _evaperation_ . As experiment 5.1 shows, when this happens, the _salt_ is left behind. Thus, the ocean's average salinity _increases_ over time. Nevertheless, the salinity of the ocean does vary. Where rivers dump water into the ocean, for example, the salinity is _Lower_ than the average salinity. ~~The average salinity of the ocean~~

indicates it is _~~Less~~_____ than even a few million years old.

The Earth is more than billions of years old

8 Saltwater freezes at a _____ temperature than does freshwater. In

fact, putting salt on ice will often _____ the ice because the salt

molecules _____ water molecules so that they move away from the

other water molecules. When the temperature gets low enough, however, even saltwater

will freeze, but the salt and water _____ as the solution freezes,

usually forming solid water that surround little pockets of concentrated saltwater called

_____ .

9 Icebergs are composed of _____ . They *do not* form as a result of

_____ water freezing. In certain polar regions, the water in the

ocean does freeze to form _____ , but that is not an iceberg. In

fact, icebergs come from _____ , which are the result of snowfall.

When a region is cold enough, the _____ does not melt away during

the summer. When new snow falls, the old snow gets packed down into what is called

_____ . As the mass of snow accumulates, it begins to slide to lower

elevations, forming a _____ .

10 As glaciers move, they might encounter warmer temperatures, where they begin to

_____ , feeding various _____ sources of the

hydrosphere. Glaciers in the polar regions often do not encounter warmer temperatures,

however, and move all the way to the ocean, where they form _____ .

When the edge of a glacier advances into the ocean, the ice _____ at some points, and large chunks of ice break off the glacier, floating away in the water.

This process, called _____ , is what makes an

_____ , approximately 90% of which is _____.

11 Soil moisture can flow down through the soil in a process called

_____ . If it travels down far enough, it will reach soil that is

completely saturated with water. The line between the saturated and unsaturated soil is

called the _____ . The depth of this line _____

over time. For example, when there is a period of very heavy rains, the depth

_____ , and when there are periods of little or no rain, the depth

_____ .

12 If a lake has a high enough salinity to consider it a saltwater lake, there are

_____ rivers taking water away from the lake. As a result, the only

way water can leave is through _____ . The

_____ is one such lake, and it has a much higher salinity than that

of the ocean.

13 Water in the atmosphere exists as either _____ or

_____ . In order for clouds to form, there must be

_____ upon which water can condense. This

condensation occurs because as air expands, it gets _____. The

scientific name for this process is _____ . Water in clouds can be

either _____ or _____ , depending on the

temperature.

14 Adiabatic cooling should not be confused with the fact that most things

_____ when they are heated. When you heat something, you are

giving it _____ . In adiabatic cooling, air is expanding *without*

being given _____ .

15 A refrigerator uses a substance that is a _____ at room

temperature. A compressor in the refrigerator compresses the gas, which

_____ it up and forms a lot of _____ .

Once compressed, the gas is released into a _____ portion of the

system, which allows it to _____ . This _____

down the contents of the refrigerator. In addition, the gas that had condensed

_____ , which further cools the system. The pipes that carry the

expanded gas are on the _____ of the refrigerator, and the pipes

that carry the compressed gas are on the _____ of the refrigerator.

16 _____ is the result of a cloud forming on the ground. Although this

used to be called _____ , that term is now generally used to refer to

a brownish haze that results from pollution. However, that brownish haze is more properly

referred to as _____ .

17 One of the real environmental problems that exists today is water

_____ , especially what is occurring to the groundwater supply.

Since nearly 50% of the United States gets its _____ from

groundwater sources, it has a direct effect on human health.

MODULE 6 SUMMARY (OPTIONAL)

1 Earth is typically divided into five regions: the atmosphere, the hydrosphere, the

_____ , the _____ , and the

_____ . The deepest region is further subdivided into the

_____ and _____ . We have learned about

the lowest regions with _____ , such as

observing how sound waves pass through the earth.

2 The earth's crust is its _____ layer of _____ .

It is separated from the mantle by the _____ ,

which is typically called the _____ for short. We have never

been able to drill _____ the crust. The crust also contains

_____ and small, solid fragments of rock and other materials

called _____. Many of the rocks of the earth's crust are

_____ , which are formed when chemical reactions cement

sediments together. Other rock types found in the crust are _____

(rock that forms from molten rock) and _____

(rock that has been changed as a result of great pressure and temperature).

3 The mantle is _____ the crust, and it is separated from the outer

core by the _____ . Its principal ingredient is

_____ . Deeper portions of the mantle have a

_____ temperature than shallower portions of the mantle. The crust

and the upper layers of the mantle form the _____ , and

directly below that is the _____ , where the rock is called

_____ because it behaves like something between a liquid and a

solid.

4 When earthquakes occur, they emit vibrations called _____ , which

travel through the earth, eventually reaching the surface. They can be detected with

_____ , which can be used to tell how the waves traveled through

the inner parts of the earth. This allows scientists to develop _____

of the earth's mantle and core, which allow us to understand their makeup.

5 The core's principal ingredient is _____ . In the outer core, the iron

is _____ , but in the inner core, it is _____ .

Nevertheless, the inner core has a _____ temperature than the outer

core. The reason the inner core is solid is because of _____ . The

boundary between the inner and outer cores is the _____ .

6 Electrical currents in the earth's core are responsible for the earth's _____ ,

the strength of which has been _____ for the past 170 years. In

addition, its direction has _____ a few times in the past. The data

indicate that at least some of these reversals have happened over a

_____ time period.

7 The earth's magnetic field deflects the vast majority of _____ that

come from the sun. Without such protection, _____ would cease

to exist as a result of the _____ of these particles. If the earth's magnetic field were too small, _____ of them would be deflected. If

it were too strong, it would cause deadly _____ that would make life

impossible. Thus, the earth has a magnetic field that is

_____ .

8 There are basically two views of how the electrical currents in the core originated, and they

are called the _____ and the _____ .

The _____ assumes that the earth is billions of years old and is

_____ when compared to the data. The_____assumes

that the earth is only thousands of years old and is _____ when

compared to the data. The fact that most scientists believe in the

_____ in spite of the data indicates that there is no such thing as an

_____ scientist. The _____ says that all planets

initially had a magnetic field, but some planets' fields have decayed away to nothing by

now. The _____ says that once a planet has a magnetic field, its

strength might change, but it will never be completely gone.

9 The theory of _____ views the earth's lithosphere as composed of

several " _____ " that all move about on the plastic rock of the

_____ . When they move away from each other,

_____ leaks up from the mantle, creating new

_____ . When they collide, one can slide under the other, generally

forming a _____ with mountains on one side. When this happens,

_____ is destroyed as it melts into the mantle. When they collide

and neither slides under the other, they _____ , forming mountains.

10 When they _____ (or shear) against each other, their edges scrape against each other. This motion can result in severe _____ . Many of our observations of _____, _____, and _____ seem to support the theory of plate tectonics. There are deep trenches at the bottom of the oceans, the characteristics of which are well described by the theory that the plates in that region of the earth are moving _____. In the end, then, most geologists believe that the plate tectonics theory is _____ .

11 The fact that the continents appear as if they fit together like a jigsaw puzzle has led some scientists to speculate that years ago, all the continents were connected in a giant supercontinent, which has been called _____ . Evidence to support this idea includes the fact that sections of rock from different continents are _____ , and they " _____" when you put the continents together the way they are assumed to have existed in _____ . Although most scientists believe that the plates have always moved _____ , a theory called "catastrophic plate tectonics" uses _____ plate movement as a result of a global catastrophe to explain how the supercontinent split in a short amount of time.

12 Vibration of the earth that results either from volcanic activity or rock masses suddenly moving along a fault is called an _____ . A fault is the _____ between two sections of rock that can _____ relative to one another. Wherever a fault exists, there is the possibility of an _____ .

13 The most successful theory regarding fault-related earthquakes is the _____ .

In this theory, as rock masses on a fault try to move relative to each other, they get

_____ on one another. As a result, they _____ .

Eventually, the rock masses _____ of each other, and

_____ they " _____ " to their normal shape.

14 The point where an earthquake begins is called the earthquake's _____ .

The _____ is the point on the surface of the earth directly above the

earthquake's focus. The study of earthquakes is called _____ , and it

uses delicate instruments called _____ that can measure vibrations

that are too small for us to notice. This has led to a scale that classifies earthquakes based

on their strength, called the _____ . This scale runs from 0 to 10,

and each step along this scale is an increase of approximately _____

in the energy of an earthquake. An earthquake that measures 5 on the Richter scale

is _____ times more energetic than one that measures 4 and

_____ less energetic than one that measures 8.

If a fault exists in which one rock mass is moving up and the other is stationary or moving

15 down, the upward-moving mass of rock will form a _____ . When two

moving rock masses push against each other with extreme force, the crust can bend in an

up-and-down, rolling pattern, forming _____ . A mountain formed by

lava leaking up through the crust from the mantle is a _____ ,

while one formed by magma that does not leave the mantle is called

_____ .

MODULE 7 SUMMARY (OPTIONAL)

1 The term "_____" refers to the condition of the earth's atmosphere (mostly the troposphere) at any particular time. _____ , on the other hand, is a steady condition that prevails day in and day out in a particular region of creation.

2 The principal factors affecting the weather are _____ ,

_____ ,

and _____ .

3 Meteorologists separate clouds into four basic groups: _____ (fluffy piles of clouds), _____ (layers of clouds), _____ (high altitude, wispy clouds), and _____ (lens-shaped clouds). You generally find each type of cloud at a _____ altitude, but a prefix of "_____" is used to indicate that a cloud type is higher than expected. In general, _____ clouds form at the highest altitudes, while _____ clouds form at the lower altitudes. A prefix of "_____" or a suffix of "_____" is also added if the cloud is dark. Dark clouds are the ones that typically bring _____ .

4 Unusually large, upward-moving wind currents can produce huge, towering _____ that most people call "thunderclouds." Cirrus clouds are composed of _____ instead of liquid water. Precipitation-producing stratus clouds are typically called _____ . Clouds that look like part cirrus/part cumulus clouds are called _____ , while clouds

that look a bit like cumulus clouds but are formed where stratus clouds normally formed

are called _____ . Finally, some clouds have the feathery

appearance of cirrus clouds, but they form flat layers like that of stratus clouds and are

called _____ .

5 Light that comes to the earth from the sun is called _____ , which

abbreviates "incoming solar radiation." The earth's _____ and its

_____ affect how much a region of the earth gets. In addition, cloud

cover can _____ the amount of incoming solar radiation. The earth

orbits the sun in an oval pattern that mathematicians call an _____ .

When the earth is at its aphelion, it is the _____ it will ever be from

the sun. When it is at its perihelion, it is _____ to the sun.

6 Because of Earth's axial tilt, sunlight shines more directly on the _____

when Earth is at aphelion. Thus, it is _____ in the Northern

Hemisphere and _____ in the Southern Hemisphere at that time. At

perihelion, sunlight shines more directly on the _____ . At that time,

then, it is _____ in the Northern Hemisphere and

_____ in the Southern Hemisphere.

7 At the two _____ , the days are _____ long in

both hemispheres. As the earth moves from the autumnal equinox (spring equinox in the

Southern Hemisphere) to the winter solstice (summer solstice in the Southern Hemisphere), the days in the Northern Hemisphere are _____ than 12 hours

and are getting _____ . In the Southern Hemisphere, the days are

_____ than 12 hours and are getting _____ . From

the winter solstice (summer solstice in the Southern Hemisphere) to the spring equinox

(autumnal equinox in the Southern Hemisphere), the days in the Northern Hemisphere are

_____ than 12 hours and are getting _____ . In

the Southern Hemisphere, the days are _____ than 12 hours and are

getting _____ .

8 Most likely, Christ was born in _____ , not December. However,

December 25 is celebrated as Christ's birthday because missionaries tried to link it to a

pagan holiday that was called the _____ .

9 Imaginary lines that run north and south across the earth are called _____ ,

while imaginary lines that run east and west across the earth are called

_____ . The latitude is _____ at the equator and

increases the _____ you move away from it. The longitude is

_____ at the prime meridian, which runs through

_____ . It increases the _____ you move away

from the prime meridian.

10 Hot air _____ . As this happens, it creates a region of

_____ pressure. Cold air _____ . As this

happens, it creates a region of _____ pressure. These effects cause

loops of winds to develop as air tries to move from _____ regions of the earth (like the poles) to _____ regions of the earth (like the

equator). These winds are then bent by the _____ , which stems from

the fact

that different parts of the earth move at different speeds. The result is prevailing winds in

the polar regions called _____ , prevailing winds in the mid latitudes

called _____ , and prevailing winds near the equator called

_____ .

11 Because of the Coriolis effect, a missile fired due north from the equator will end up

hitting a target _____ of its launch site, while a missile fired due

south from near the North Pole will end up hitting a target _____ of

its launch site. The Coriolis effect, however, is _____ to significantly

affect how water drains in a basin.

12 Prevailing wind patterns can be easily disrupted by _____ . Examples

of such winds would be a _____ near the ocean shore, which tends

to blow during the day, and a _____ , which tends to blow near the

ocean shore during the night.

13 An air mass is a large body of air with relatively uniform _____ ,

_____ , and _____ . The three basic types

of air masses are _____ , _____ , and

_____ . _____ air masses are very cold

and dry. _____ air masses are warm and moist, while

_____ air masses are cold and moist. _____ air

masses are warm and dry, while _____ air masses are cold (but not as

cold as arctic air masses) and dry.

14 A weather front is a _____ between two air masses. The four basic

types are _____ , _____ ,

_____ , and _____ .

15 When a cold front moves in, _____ clouds are usually formed by the

warm air _____ in response to the cold air mass. The temperature

in the region tends to _____ . Cold fronts generally carry the most

_____ weather systems, including thunderstorms.

16 When a warm front moves in, the warm air tends to _____ above the

cooler air that was in the region. This usually causes a progression of clouds from cirrus

to _____ to stratus to _____ , which generally

heralds a _____ and _____ rain as well as

_____ temperatures.

17 Occluded fronts occur when a_____ meets up with a slower-

moving _____ . They usually result in slow, steady rains followed by

_____ .

18 A stationary front generally results in weather that doesn't _____

much for a long period of time.

MODULE 8 SUMMARY (OPTIONAL)

1 Eventually, all the water that evaporates into the atmosphere falls back to the earth, mostly in the form of _____ . However, water can also leave the atmosphere and return to the earth as _____ or

_____ .

2 By far, the most common form of precipitation is _____ . There are two theories about how it forms in clouds. The _____ process deals with how rain is formed in cold clouds. The ice crystals in these clouds grow _____ until they can no longer remain _____ in the air. As they fall, they typically pick up more _____ , growing even heavier. Eventually, these ice crystals become so big that they _____ , which results in several ice crystals falling through the cloud. Each of these fragments, until there are billions of _____ falling from the cloud. As they descend, they melt and form _____ .

3 In warm clouds, meteorologists think that rain forms according to the

_____ . In this theory, each cloud contains many water droplets. As _____ in the cloud move these droplets around, they _____ with other water droplets. Sometimes the droplets stick together, forming a _____ water droplet. Eventually, a water droplet gets big enough to start _____ through the cloud.

4 Drizzle usually forms in _____ clouds. Sleet is different from freezing

rain because sleet is frozen _____ it hits the ground, while freezing

rain is not. _____ is formed when an ice crystal or raindrop is blown

back into the cloud by an upward gust of wind. If blown high enough, the raindrop

will _____ , or the ice crystal will get _____ .

Depending on the wind conditions, the ice crystal might be blown back up into the clouds

_____ times. Eventually, it gets so big that the upward gusts of wind

are _____ strong enough to push it back up into the clouds, and it

falls to the earth. Snow starts out as precipitation from a _____ cloud.

As the ice crystals fall from the clouds, they _____ , freezing and

growing into bigger ice crystals.

5 A thunderstorm begins with a current of rising air, called an _____.

As the air rises, water condenses onto cloud condensation nuclei, which actually

_____ the cloud condensation nuclei, making the current of rising air

stronger. This is the _____ stage of the thunderstorm. Eventually, the

water droplets and/or ice crystals in the cloud become too _____ ,

and it begins to rain. This marks the _____ stage of the

thunderstorm. As the rain falls, it causes winds that blow downward, which are called

_____. These winds eventually overpower the rising currents of air

that started the storm, and the entire area is full of only _____ . This

marks the _____ stage of the thunderstorm. A single thunderstorm

cell typically lasts for less than _____ minutes, but a thunderstorm

might be composed of _____ cells so that the storm lasts longer.

6 Lightning forms because a charge _____ in a cloud causes charge to build up on the _____ . The positive charges on the ground attract some negative charges from the cloud, forming a _____ . The closeness of the negative charges forces the positive charges up, making the _____ , which is the most powerful part of the lightning strike. The _____ that you hear is the result of air that has been superheated by the return stroke. Although this kind of lightning (called _____ lightning) forms lightning bolts, _____ lightning lights up the sky in big sheets.

7 Tornadoes start as the result of updrafts that form _____ . In the first stage of their development, known as the _____ stage, the updraft of air forming a cumulonimbus cloud begins being hit by winds blowing in a different direction at higher altitudes. Combined with the updraft, this causes a funnel of air to form, with air whirling both around and up. This is often called a _____ . The funnel of air then touches the ground, starting the _____ stage of the tornado. Once the funnel touches the ground, it sucks debris up into the funnel, which darkens the tornado. This marks the _____ stage. It is in this stage that the tornado is most destructive. Eventually, the forces that hold the vortex together dissipate, and the tornado gets smaller, entering its _____ stage. Finally, the tornado weakens to the point that it is no longer visible, and it slowly dies out in the _____ stage. When tornadoes form over the water, the result is a _____ , which is _____ than a tornado that forms over land. A _____ is even weaker, forming as a result of temperature differences between the ground and the air above it.

8 Hurricanes are more properly called _____ because they always start in the tropics. They begin as a _____ that is fed by the warm, moist air of the tropical sea. If the rotating winds reach a sustained speed of 23 miles per hour, it is "upgraded" to a _____ . If the winds reach a sustained speed of 39 miles per hour, the depression is "upgraded" again to a _____ . Finally, if the winds reach 74 miles per hour, it becomes a full-fledged hurricane. There are _____ categories of hurricanes, which are based on the wind speeds in the storm. The most pronounced feature of a hurricane is its _____ , and the clouds spin around the eye _____ in the Northern Hemisphere and _____ in the Southern Hemisphere. The eye is actually a place of _____ in the midst of the storm.

9 _____ (which stands for "radio detection and ranging"), emits _____ waves at a rate of several hundred per second. As those waves encounter objects, they _____ off the objects and head back toward the radar unit. The time it takes for the waves to travel to an object and then bounce back indicates the _____ to the object. In addition, differences between the outgoing and returning waves provide information that can determine whether a cloud is made up of _____ (a cold cloud) or _____ (a warm cloud). _____ is a well-known tool in both weather and law enforcement. Traffic police use it to determine the _____ of automobiles, while meteorologists use it to measure the _____ of winds and air masses.

10 Weather _____ take data continuously all over the world and give us an accurate, _____ picture of the weather fronts and patterns that exist on a day-to-day basis. They also provide strong evidence that global warming is _____ happening.

11 Weather data is often summarized on a _____ map that allows meteorologists to track fronts and atmospheric pressure. The thin black lines on such a map are called _____ , and they represent regions of equal _____ pressure. An "H" on such a map indicates an area of _____ pressure, while an "L" represents _____ pressure. Isobars represent _____ pressure the farther they are from an "L" and _____ pressure the farther they are from an "H."

12 If a thick line on a weather map has only triangles on it, it represents a _____ front, and the way the triangles point tells you the _____ in which the front travels. If it has only ovals on it, the line represents a _____ front, and the side the ovals are on tells you the _____ in which the front travels. If the line has both ovals and circles on the same side, it represents an _____ front, and once again, the side that the symbols are on tells you the _____ in which the front travels. Finally, if the line has ovals on one side and triangles on another, it represents a _____ front.

MODULE 9 SUMMARY (OPTIONAL)

1 Every science relies on the science of _____ . As a result, we call it the

most _____ of all the sciences. The science of

_____ is the branch of physics that deals with analyzing and

understanding objects in motion, the _____ that are applied to those

objects, and the _____ that exists in them.

2 When studying motion, one must define a _____ , which is a point

against which position is measured. If an object's position relative to this point is

_____, the object is in motion relative to that point. Because motion

depends on the reference point, all motion is _____ .

3 The units for speed and velocity are composed of a _____ unit

divided by a _____ unit. In base metric units, speed is given in

_____ . While _____ simply tells you how

quickly an object is moving, _____ tells you how quickly an object is

moving *and* the direction in which it moves. Thus, speed is a _____

quantity, while velocity is a _____ quantity. Speed can be calculated

with the equation:

_____

4 When objects travel in the same direction, their relative speed is the

_____ between their individual speeds. When they travel in opposite

directions, their relative speed is the _____ of their individual speeds.

5 The time rate of change of an object's velocity is its _____. The units

for this quantity are composed of a _____ unit divided by a

_____ unit _____ . In base metric units, it is given

in _____ . It is a _____ quantity because it

contains directional information. It can be calculated with the equation:

_____

6 An object with an unchanging speed can still have acceleration, provided that its

_____ is changing. In physics, the term "acceleration" can also mean

that an object is _____ because acceleration is simply the change in

velocity, and a decrease in velocity is still a change. If an object is speeding up, its

acceleration is in the _____ as its velocity. If it is slowing down, its

acceleration is in the _____ as compared to its velocity.

7 When an object falls solely under the influence of gravity, we say that it is in

_____ . In such a situation, the acceleration is equal to

_____ in metric units and _____ English units.

This acceleration is _____ of the characteristics of the object. Thus,

in true free fall, a feather and a bowling ball will fall with the _____

acceleration.

8 When an object is in free fall, the distance it drops can be calculated with the equation:

_____

9 Although we generally treat objects falling near the surface of the earth as if they were in free fall, _____ impedes the fall of all objects. Thus, things don't truly free fall unless there is no _____ . However, for most objects, the effect of _____ can be ignored. Thus, when most objects fall near the surface of the earth, we can assume they are in _____.

10 When doing an experiment in which error is a known problem, you can reduce the effects of error by making _____ measurements and _____ the results.

Solve the Following Problems

11 What is the speed of a boat that travels 20 miles in 45 minutes? Please answer in miles per hour and show all work.

12 Label each quantity as a vector or scalar quantity. Also, identify it as speed, distance, velocity, acceleration, or none of these.

    a. 10 meters/second^2 north

    b. 1.2 meters/second

    c. 3.4 feet/hour and slowing

    d. 2.3 miles/minute west

13 A sports car goes from a velocity of zero to a velocity of 15 meters per second east in 2.1 seconds. What is the car's acceleration?

14 What is the height of a building (in meters) if it takes a rock 3.8 seconds to drop from its roof?

15 A car and a truck are traveling north on a highway. The truck has a speed of 42 miles per hour, and the car has a speed of 37 miles per hour. If the truck is ahead of the car, what is the relative velocity?

37 mph

42 mph

16 If an object travels for 10 minutes with a constant velocity of 11 miles per hour north, what is the acceleration?

17 A car that is traveling at 55 miles per hour south brakes suddenly. It takes 3.5 seconds for the car to come to a full stop. What is the acceleration, in miles per hour²? (1 hour = 3600 seconds)

18 How far (in feet) did a dropped rock fall if it took 2.3 seconds to reach the ground?

MODULE 10 SUMMARY (OPTIONAL)

1 Sir Isaac Newton discovered _____ laws of motion, developed a

theory describing _____ , did the famous prism experiment that

showed white light is composed of many _____ , and in order to

help his scientific investigations, he developed a new kind of mathematics that we now

call "_____." He was also a devoutly _____

man who spent as much time studying the _____ as he did studying

science.

2 Newton's three laws of motion are:

I.

II.

III.

3 The tendency of an object to resist changes in its velocity is referred to as

_____ . When a bomb is dropped from an airplane, the bomb

_____ hit the ground directly below where the airplane dropped it.

Instead, it continues to move in the _____ that the plane was moving

when the bomb was dropped because of Newton's _____ law of

motion. Thus, a bomber must drop the bomb _____ it is above the

target.

371

4 The reason Aristotle made so many mistakes when describing motion is that he did not

know about the existence of _____ , a force that opposes motion and

results from the contact of two _____ . This force exists because on

the atomic scale, all surfaces are _____ . This affects how close the

molecules can get to one another, which affects how much they are

_____ to each other. The more they are _____

to one another, the stronger the frictional force. When this force opposes motion once

the motion has already started, we call it _____. When it opposes

the initiation of motion, we call it _____ . Between these two forces,

_____ is greater than _____ .

5 A force is essentially a push or a pull exerted on an object in an effort to change that

object's _____ . You can calculate force with the equation:

_____

The units of force are composed of a _____ unit times a

_____ unit divided by a _____ unit squared. The

standard unit for force is _____ , which is also called the "Newton."

6 When multiple forces act on an object, forces in the same direction are

_____ and forces in opposite directions are _____.

Since friction always opposes motion, the frictional force will always be

_____ from the force that is being used to cause motion.

7 When you fire a gun, it "kicks" back toward you. That "kick" is the result of Newton's

_____ law of motion. When you pull the trigger, you cause a

_____ to take place in the chamber. That reaction produces a lot of

_____ and _____ . The gas is under pressure, so

it exerts a force on the _____ , pushing the bullet out at an amazing

speed. In response, the _____ pushes back against the gas in the

gun.

Solve the Following Problems

8 Ignoring friction, what force is necessary to move a 25.0-kg object with an acceleration of

34.5 m/sec² to the west?

9 Ignoring friction, what force is necessary to move a 125.0-kg object with a constant

velocity of 3.4 m/sec?

10 An object moves with a constant velocity to the north. If the static friction between the object and the floor is 25 Newtons, while the kinetic friction is 15 Newtons, what force is being applied to the object?

11 In order to move a 65-kilogram object, a force of more than 40 Newtons must be exerted. Once it is moving, a force of only 30 Newtons accelerates the object at 0.1 meters per second² to the west. What is the force of static friction between the object and the surface upon which it sits? What is the force of kinetic friction?

12 The static frictional force between a 95-kilogram object and the floor is 45 Newtons. The kinetic frictional force is only 22 Newtons. How many Newtons of force must be exerted to get the object moving? What force must be exerted to accelerate the box at 0.5 meters per second² to the south?

13 Three forces (besides friction) act on a 50-kg object: 35 Newtons east, 45 Newtons east, and 10 Newtons west. The object accelerates at 0.10 meters per second² to the east. What is the kinetic frictional force between the object and the floor?

14 In order to move a box, a worker gets it moving by exerting just slightly more than 75 Newtons of force. To keep it moving at a constant velocity west, however, he exerts 45 Newtons force to the west. What are the static and kinetic frictional forces between the box and the floor?

MODULE 11 SUMMARY (OPTIONAL)

1 The weakest of the four fundamental forces in creation is the _____

force, and it is always attractive. The _____ force exists between

charged particles. The _____ force governs certain radioactive

processes in atoms. Physicists have actually shown that _____ force

and the weak force are different facets of the same force. Thus, scientists call this force

the _____ force. The _____ force is responsible

for holding the center of the atom (called the _____) together.

Although this force is strong, its range is very, very _____ .

2 The three general principles contained in Newton's universal law of gravitation are:

I.

II.

III.

3 Although the gravitational force is _____ , it can be substantial when

at least one of the objects involved has a large _____. In

addition, the gravitational forces exerted by two objects on one another are

_____ . Thus, a ball is attracted to the earth because

_____ applies a gravitational force on the ball. At the same time, the

_____ applies an _____ but

_____ force on the _____.

4 _____ force is the force necessary to make an object move in a circle, and it is always directed _____ to the velocity of the object, which means it points to the _____ of the circle. Since the direction of the object moving in a circle is continually _____ , it experiences _____ regardless of whether or not its speed stays constant. Centrifugal force is _____ a real force. It is simply a consequence of _____ .

5 If the centripetal force operating on an object moving in a circle suddenly disappears, the object begins traveling _____ , in the direction it was moving the instant the force disappeared. Centripetal force can be summed up with three basic principles:

    I.

    II.

    III.

6 The gravitational force acts to hold the planets and their moons in an orderly arrangement which we call the _____ . The sun's _____ applies a centripetal force to the planets, allowing them to travel around the sun in roughly _____ orbits. The closest planet to the sun is _____ , and continuing out from there, you find _____ , _____ , and _____ . Next you find the solar system's highest concentration of _____. As a result, this region

is often called the _____ . Beyond that you find

_____ , _____ , _____

, and _____ . Typically, the planets of the solar system are placed

into one of two groups: the _____ (Mercury, Venus, Earth, and

Mars) and the _____ (Jupiter, Saturn, Uranus, and

Neptune). Of all the planets, _____ is the hottest because of its

_____ . _____ was once called a planet, but it is

now called a _____ . It was demoted when a larger

_____ (KBO) named Eris was found.

7 When an object orbits around a planet, we call that object a _____

of the planet. All planets except Mercury and Venus have at least one natural

_____ , but most have more than one. Saturn, Uranus, Jupiter, and

Neptune also have _____ , the most pronounced of which are around

Saturn. They are actually composed of _____ of rock, ice, and frozen

gases.

8 Variations in a body's motion are called _____ , and a careful study of

them led to the discovery of the planet _____ . When they happen to

an asteroid, it can be thrown out of its standard orbit and toward Earth. When it intersects

Earth's orbit, it is called a _____ . When it actually hits Earth's

atmosphere, it becomes white-hot, making brilliant streaks of light in the sky. At that

point, scientists call it a _____ . The intense heat usually breaks it up,

except for a few small pieces that fall to the ground and are called _____ .

9 Comets are called "dirty _____" because they are mostly composed of dust grains, chunks of dirt, and _____ . When a comet passes close to the sun, the solid part of the comet is called the _____ , and the "fuzzy" atmosphere around it is called the _____ , which can form a long, glowing tail in the night sky. _____ comets typically don't go farther from the sun than the planet _____ and take less than 200 years to make an orbit. _____ comets typically have orbits that extend to the planet _____ or beyond and take more than 200 years to orbit the sun. The _____ contains many bodies that have some characteristics of comets and is thought by many to be a source of _____ comets. There are, however, problems with that view. Scientists forced to believe that the solar system is billions of years old must also believe in the _____ as a source for _____ comets, although there is no evidence for its existence.

10 There are essentially two theories on what causes the gravitational force: the _____ and the _____ . The _____ says that gravity is a consequence of how mass bends both space and time, while the _____ states that gravity is a result of the fact that objects with mass exchange particles called _____ . Most physicists would say that the _____ is better, since it has some direct evidence supporting it.

11 The Greeks thought all planets (and the sun) orbited the _____ .

This is called the _____ view of the solar system. As time went on,

observations just couldn't be made consistent with this view, so scientists (like Copernicus)

suggested the _____ view that the planets orbit the sun.

Solve the Following Problems

12 The gravitational force between two objects ($mass_1$ = 5 kg, $mass_2$ = 2 kg) is measured

when the objects are 5 centimeters apart. If the distance between them is increased to 10

centimeters, how does the new gravitational attraction compare to the first one that was

measured?

13 The gravitational force between two objects ($mass_1$ = 5 kg, $mass_2$ = 2 kg) is measured

when the objects are 5 centimeters apart. If $mass_1$ is changed to 10 kg and $mass_2$ is

changed to 6 kg, how does the new gravitational attraction compare to the first one that

was measured?

14 The gravitational force between two objects (mass$_1$ = 5 kg, mass$_2$ = 2 kg) is measured when the objects are 5 centimeters apart. The masses are then changed to mass$_1$ = 10 kg, mass$_1$ = 16 kg, and the distance between them is increased to 20 cm. How does the new gravitational attraction compare to the first one that was measured?

MODULE 12 SUMMARY (OPTIONAL)

1 Because of the genius of _____ , we now know that

the force between charged particles and the force between magnets are both facets of

the same force, called the _____ . As was the case with

Newton, Maxwell studied science as a means of serving _____ .

2 The three principles of the electromagnetic force are:

    I.

    II.

    III.

3 The electromagnetic force is significantly _____ than the

gravitational force. It is produced by the _____ of small "packages"

of light called _____ . The more charge a particle has, the more

_____ it can exchange. This tells you why the electromagnetic force

between charged particles is directly proportional to the charge of the particle. When you

randomly throw a ball at person, the chance of you hitting that person is

_____ proportional to the _____ of the distance

between you. Thus, the ability for _____ to exchange photons also is

inversely proportional to the square of the distance between them.

4 In an atom, there are as many _____ (positive charges) as there are _____ (negative charges). As a result, atoms are electrically _____ . When an atom loses _____ , it ends up with a net positive charge and is called a positive _____ . When an atom picks up extra _____ , it ends up with a net negative charge and is called a negative _____ .

5 When you charge an object by allowing it to come into contact with an object that already has an electric charge, you are charging by _____ . This gives the newly charged object the _____ type of charge (positive or negative) as the original object. When you charge an object without direct contact between the object and a charge, you are charging by _____ , and the newly charged object typically has a charge _____ that of the original charge.

6 A battery _____ electrical charge. One side of the battery is a source of electrons, so it is considered _____ . The other is the place where the electrons want to go, so it is considered _____ . When the two sides of a battery are hooked together with a metal, _____ will flow through the metal from the _____ side of the battery to the _____ side. A battery's _____ tells you how hard the battery "pushes" _____ from one side to the other.

7 The amount of charge that travels past a fixed point in an electric circuit each second

is called the _____ in the circuit. It is usually measured in

_____ , which are abbreviated as " _____ "

or " _____ ." Both the _____ (amps) and the

_____ (volts) of a circuit are needed to know how powerful the

circuit is.

8 Current that flows from the positive side of the battery to the negative side is called

_____ . This is the way current is drawn in circuit diagrams, even

though it is _____ . The ability of a material to impede the flow of

charge is called that material's _____ , and it converts the energy

of the charge flowing through the circuit into _____ and

sometimes _____ . The _____ of metal, the

_____ of the metal, and the _____ of the

metal all affect its resistance. The longer the metal, the _____ the

resistance, and the wider the metal, the _____ the resistance.

9 The same number of _____ flow out of a toaster as the number

that flow into it. The toaster does use up something, however. It uses

_____ . As electrons flow through a circuit, the collisions they

experience convert the _____ produced by the electromagnetic force

into _____ .

10 A circuit that does not have a complete connection between the two sides of the power source is called an _____ . Current _____ flow through an open circuit. This is how a switch works. When the switch is "off," the circuit is _____ , and no current can flow. When the switch is "on," a _____ is made, and current begins to flow.

11 When light bulbs are hooked in a circuit in _____ , one broken light bulb will cause them all to go out. When light bulbs are hooked in _____ , the other light bulbs will still work even if one or more break.

12 All magnetic force results from the movement of _____ particles. The atoms of most materials are not _____ , so the electrons in the material have random motion. This causes the individual magnetic fields that result from that motion to _____ . The result, then, is _____ magnetic behavior. However, certain materials under certain conditions can have their atoms arranged so that the electrons have the _____ general motion. When that happens, the result is a _____.

13 All magnets have two poles: the _____ and the _____ . Opposite poles _____ one another, and like poles _____ one another. Because all magnets have two poles, they are sometimes called _____ . The strength of a magnet depends on what _____ of the atoms in the material are _____ . The larger the percentage, the _____ the pole of a magnet.

Solve the Following Problems

 The force between two charges is measured when the objects are 5 centimeters apart. The charges are then doubled, and the distance between them is increased to 20 cm. How does the new force compare to the first one that was measured?

 The force between two charges is measured when the objects are 5 centimeters apart. The charges on each are cut in half, and the distance between them is decreased to 2.5 cm. How does the new force compare to the first one that was measured?

 Draw the conventional current and the flow of actual electrons in the following circuit:

17 Draw the conventional current in the following circuits:

a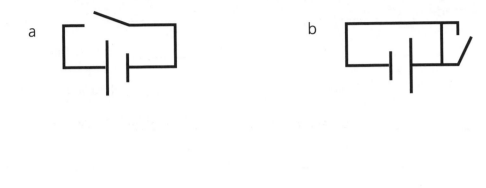

b

c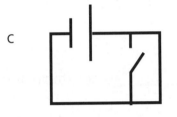

MODULE 13 SUMMARY (OPTIONAL)

1 Atoms are made up of _____ , _____ , and

_____ . The _____ is the smallest and least

massive of the three. It also has a _____ electrical charge. The

_____ is next in terms of mass. It is about 2,000 times more massive

than the _____ and has a _____ electrical charge.

The _____ is the heaviest of the three, being just a bit more massive

than the _____ . It has _____ electrical charge.

By itself, the _____ is not stable. If it is not in the nucleus of an atom,

it will decay into a _____ , an _____ , and an

antineutrino in a matter of minutes.

2 A _____ is a schematic description of a system that accounts for its

known properties. The _____ model of the atom has the

_____ and _____ packed together in the center

of the atom, which is called the _____ . The

_____ orbit the _____ , much like the planets in

the solar system orbit the sun. Although this model is partially _____ ,

it is still the first model students learn when it comes to the atom. The more correct

model is called the _____ model, but it is a bit too complex

to learn right away. Regardless of the model, we know that atoms (and therefore all of

matter) are mostly empty _____ .

3 One of the most important characteristics of an atom is its number of protons, which is

also called its _____ . This tells you what kind of atom it is. Atoms

have equal numbers of protons and _____ , so the atomic number

also tells you how many _____ an atom has. The

_____ is the sum of the numbers of neutrons and protons in the

nucleus, so once you know the number of protons and the _____ ,

you can figure out how many _____ are in the nucleus.

4 A collection of atoms that all have the same _____ of protons is

called an "element." On the periodic chart, the chemical symbol for an element is usually

the first _____ or _____ letters from the

_____ or _____ name of the element. Looking

at the periodic chart, you can see that oxygen (O) has an atomic number of

_____ . This means it has _____ electrons and _____ protons.

An ^{18}O atom, then, has _____ neutrons, while ^{16}O has _____ neutrons. Since ^{16}O

and ^{18}O all have the same number of protons but different numbers of neutrons, they are

_____ . In the same way, of the following list of atoms: ^{40}Ar, ^{40}Ca,

^{41}K, ^{41}Ca, ^{45}Sc, and ^{42}Ca, the isotopes are _____ .

5 If you were to draw an atom of ^{31}P according to the Bohr model, you would start by

drawing a nucleus that had _____ and _____ .

It would also have _____ electrons orbiting the nucleus in the

nearest orbit, _____ electrons orbiting the nucleus in the next orbit

out, and _____ electrons orbiting the nucleus in a third orbit that

389

was farther from the nucleus. In the same way, the Bohr model of ^{84}Sr would have

_____ and _____ in the nucleus. There would

be _____ electrons in the first Bohr orbit, _____

electrons in the next, _____ electrons in the third Bohr orbit, and

_____ electrons in the fourth Bohr orbit.

6 Although protons are positively charged and thus should _____ one

another, experiments have shown that they exist packed together inside the

_____ . This led scientists to speculate that there is a

_____ force that is attractive at very short distances and is strong

enough to overcome the repulsive electromagnetic force between protons. Hideki Yukawa

showed that the exchange of tiny particles called _____ could

account for such a force, and he gave a rough prediction of their mass. The detection of

_____ -lived particles with just that mass confirmed the existence of

the force.

7 The nuclear force is a short-range force because pions exist for only a

_____ time. Thus, if two protons (or a proton and a neutron) want to

exchange a pion, they must do it _____ . The nuclear force is actually

a manifestation of the _____ force, which is also manifested in the

exchange of _____ between quarks. This allows

_____ and _____ to exist.

8 The weak force governs _____ . An atom with a nucleus that is not

stable is called a _____ isotope. The three main ways unstable nuclei can decay is through _____ decay (where a neutron turns into a

proton, _____ , and antineutrino), _____ decay

(where the nucleus emits a ^{4}He nucleus), and _____ decay (where

energy is released in the form of a high-energy photon).

9 The hydrogen isotope known as "tritium" (^{3}H) undergoes beta decay. The daughter

product is _____ . When the isotope _____

undergoes beta decay, the daughter product is ^{32}S. When ^{133}Xe undergoes beta decay,

the daughter product is _____ . In each case, a

_____ (electron) and an antineutrino are also produced.

10 When ^{238}U undergoes alpha decay, the daughter product is _____ .

When _____ undergoes alpha decay, ^{218}Po is produced. When ^{210}Po

undergoes alpha decay, the daughter product is _____ . In each

case, a _____ nucleus is also produced.

11 When ^{60}Ni is produced by the beta decay of _____ , it has excess

energy. The ^{60}Ni gets rid of that excess energy by radioactive decay, but it stays ^{60}Ni. Thus,

it decays by _____ decay.

12 The _____ of a radioactive isotope is the time it takes for half of the

original sample to decay. Consider, for example, ^{239}Np, which has a half-life of 2 days.

If you start with 1,000 grams of ^{239}Np, you will have _____ grams

left after 2 days and _____ grams left after 4 days. In 10 days, you would have

_____ grams left. In _____ days, you would

have only about 0.977 grams left.

13 Even though a sample of radioactive isotope never really goes away completely,

at some point, the amount of radioactive isotope left is so small that it can be

_____ . If we keep a radioactive sample around long enough, then, it

will _____ to be radioactive, for all practical purposes.

14 Radioactive dating is the process by which scientists use the _____

of certain substances to determine how old an object is. For example, in carbon dating,

scientists use the fact that _____ decays with a half-life of 5,700

years. Because living organisms continually exchange _____

with their surroundings, while an organism is alive, it contains the same amount of

_____ as does the _____ around it. When the

organism dies, however, that exchange _____ , and the amount of

_____ begins to decrease as a result of radioactive decay. Thus, if

you know how much _____ was in the _____

when an organism died, you can determine how long ago death occurred by looking at

the difference between the _____ in the dead organism and the

amount that was in the atmosphere when it died. The difference is assumed to be the

result of _____ , and using the known half-life, you can determine

the _____ that elapsed since the organism died.

15 The main problem with carbon dating is determining the _____

of ^{14}C in the organism when it died. Scientists can use _____ to

measure the amount of ^{14}C in the atmosphere at a given year, and that gives them

the ability to make a good assumption about the _____ of ^{14}C

in the organism when it died. However, the oldest tree ring analyzed in this way is

_____ years old, so carbon dating is really only reliable for things that

are _____ years old or younger.

16 Other radioactive dating methods use similar _____ , and the fact

that many radioactive dates are in conflict with each other or with generally accepted

dates indicates the _____ are poor.

MODULE 14 SUMMARY (OPTIONAL)

1 In a wave, there are both _____ (the highest points on the wave)

and _____ (the lowest point on the wave). The distance between the

crests (or the distance between the troughs) is called the _____ ,

and it is symbolized with the Greek letter _____ . The height of the

wave is called the _____ . The _____ of a wave

indicates how many waves hit a certain point every second.

2 Frequency and wavelength can be related to one another through the equation:

_____ ,

In this equation, "f" is the _____ of the wave, "v" is the

_____ of the wave, and λ is the _____ .

The units for _____ are 1/sec, which are typically abbreviated as

_____ .

3 There are two basic forms that waves can take. A _____ is a wave

with a direction of propagation that is perpendicular to its direction of oscillation. A

_____ is a wave with a direction of propagation that is parallel

to its direction of oscillation. In a _____ , the places where the

medium "bunches up" are called _____ , while the "spread out"

sections are called _____ .

4 _____ are longitudinal waves that generally oscillate

_____ . When those waves reach the _____

membrane of the ear, the membrane vibrates. Those vibrations are then transmitted to

your _____ , which interprets them as _____ .

5 The speed of sound in air is dependent on the air's _____ , and it can

be found using the equation:

_____ .

Since the speed of light is significantly _____ than the speed of sound,

you can see a faraway event _____ you hear any sound associated

with it. Sound travels _____ in liquids than it does in gases, and it

travels _____ in solids than it does in liquids.

6 If an object travels in a medium faster than the speed of sound in that medium, we say

that the object is traveling at a _____ speed. Typically, we use the

_____ number to denote such speeds. A rocket traveling at

_____ 3, for example, is traveling at three times the speed of

sound. The sound produced as a result of an object traveling faster than sound is called a

_____ .

7 The _____ of a sound wave is governed primarily by its

frequency, while the volume is determined mostly by its _____ .

When a singer sings low notes, for example, the sounds waves she produces have

_____ frequency. When she sings high notes, the sound waves she

makes have a _____ frequency. When the singer is singing softly, the

sound waves she produces have a _____ amplitude, and when she

sings loudly, the sound waves she makes have a _____ amplitude.

8 Longitudinal waves with frequencies that can be detected by the human ear are called

_____ waves. Waves with frequencies higher than what the human

ear can sense are called _____ waves, and waves with frequencies

lower than what the human ear can detect are called _____ waves.

9 The fact that the pitch of a car's horn changes as the car passes by you is a result of the

_____ . This effect exists because as a sound source moves, the

waves in front of the source _____ together, producing a wave

with a _____ frequency than what you would hear if the source

were stationary. The waves behind a moving source are _____ out,

resulting in a frequency _____ than what you would hear if the

source were stationary.

10 The bel scale measures the _____ of a sound wave, which is

determined by the _____ . In this scale, each unit corresponds to a

factor of _____ increase in the intensity of the sound wave. Thus, a

sound wave that measure 7 bels is _____ times more intense than a

sound wave that measures 4 bels. The more common measurement associated with this

scale is the decibel. It takes _____ decibels to make a bel. As a result,

a sound measuring 80 decibels has an intensity of _____ bels.

11 Sound waves used to probe the inside of the earth are typically

_____ waves, while sound waves used to measure distances and

image things inside the human body are typically _____ waves.

Another use of such waves is _____ , a technique used both by the military and by animals such as bats. Despite our best efforts, however, the bat's _____ is significantly more _____ than anything made as a result of human science and technology.

Solve the Following Problems

12 What is the frequency of a wave that travels at a speed of 5 meters per second and has a wavelength of 1.5 meters?

13 A wave whose wavelength is 0.15 m travels with a speed of 150 meters per second. What is its frequency?

14 What is the speed of sound in air that has a temperature of 22 °C?

15 You hear the thunder from a lightning flash 2.3 seconds after you see the flash. If the air has a temperature of 11 °C, how far away did the lightning strike occur?

16 You see lightning, and then hear the thunder 1.3 seconds later. If the air has a temperature of 18 °C, how far away did the lightning strike?

17 One sound has a level of 20 decibels. The other has a level of 60 decibels. How many times more intense is the second sound?

18 An amplifier can multiply the intensity of a sound by 1,000. If a 30-decibel sound goes in, how many decibels will the sound be after the amplifier has amplified it?

MODULE 15 SUMMARY (OPTIONAL)

1 In the _____ theory of light, a beam of light behaves the same as a stream of particles that all move in the same direction. In the _____ theory, light is considered a wave. Modern scientists believe that light has a _____ nature, acting both like a _____ and a _____ . In the _____ theory, light is basically viewed as tiny packets of waves.

2 Because of the work of James Clerk Maxwell, a light wave is considered a _____ wave composed of an oscillating _____ field and a _____ field that oscillates perpendicular to the _____ field. As a result, light waves are typically called _____ .

3 Although the speed of light does _____ depend on temperature, it does depend on _____ through which the light passes. In liquids light travels _____ than it does in air, and in solids light travels _____ than it does in liquids. Einstein's special theory of relativity says that the speed of light in a vacuum represents the _____ speed that can ever be attained by any object that has mass.

4 The wavelength of visible light determines its _____ . The 7 basic colors in the rainbow, in order of increasing wavelength, are: _____ , _____ , _____ , _____ ,

_____ , _____ , and _____.

While the light we can see with our eyes is part of the   spectrum of light, the collection

of all electromagnetic waves in creation is called the _____ spectrum.

5 Ultraviolet light, X-rays, and gamma rays have wavelengths _____

than visible light. Although they have so much energy that they can

_____ living tissue, there are some uses for them. Infrared light,

microwaves, television waves, and radio waves have wavelengths

_____ than visible light.

6 When light bounces off an obstacle, we call it _____ . When this

happens, the angle of incidence will _____ the angle of

_____ . Images form in a mirror because light that

_____ off a mirror is detected by an eye, and the

_____ that receives the eye's electrical impulses extends the light

_____ to form an image behind the mirror. The image is, of course,

_____ . It is simply a result of the fact that the brain interprets light

as traveling in a _____ line.

7 When a wave enters an obstacle, it usually _____ in response to its

change in speed. When this happens, we say that the wave has been

_____ . When light enters a substance in which it must slow down,

the light ray will bend _____ a line perpendicular to the surface

it strikes. When light enters a substance in which it speeds up, the light ray will bend

_____ a line perpendicular to the surface it strikes. When you are looking at an object underwater, it will appear to be in a location that is

_____ from its actual location because the light rays

_____ when they leave the water to hit your eyes.

8 When white light hits a water droplet in the air, some _____ and

some _____ into the water droplet. Since the amount of

_____ depends partially on the _____ of the

light involved, this separates the white light into its colors. As the light travels through the

water droplet, it eventually hits the other side. A portion of the light

_____ out of the water droplet, but a portion

_____ . The _____ light travels to the other side

of the droplet, where a portion is _____ and a portion is

_____ . The portion that is _____ has its

wavelengths separated even more because the amount of _____

depends in part on the wavelength of light. With this second _____ ,

the light has been separated enough for us to distinguish the colors. As a result, the best

way to see a rainbow is for the sun to be _____ you.

9 When a lens focuses horizontally traveling light rays through a single point (called the

_____ point), we call it a _____ lens. The sides

of such a lens have a _____ shape. When a lens bends horizontally

traveling light rays so that they begin traveling away from each other, we call it a

_____ lens. The sides of such a lens have a _____

shape.

10 The most elegant application of a converging lens in all of God's creation can be seen in

the _____ . The eye is covered by a thin, transparent substance called

the _____ . Light enters the eye through the _____ ,

which is essentially an opening left by the _____ . When you are in

the presence of _____ light, the _____ closes

down to allow only a small amount of light into the eye. When there is

_____ light, the _____ opens wide, allowing a

larger percentage of the light in. Once light enters the _____ , it is

focused by a _____ lens. The light is focused onto the

_____ , which is made up of light-sensitive cells called

_____ and _____ . When these cells sense light

hitting them, they send electrical messages down the _____ nerve

to the _____ , which decodes the messages and forms them into

images.

11 In order to focus light onto the retina, the eye's lens actually _____ .

This is done through the action of the _____ , which squeezes or

expands the lens. Human science cannot make a lens as _____ as

that which you find in the eye.

12 If you are _____ , your eye can use its ciliary muscle to change the

lens enough to keep the image of objects close to you focused on the retina. However, as

the object moves _____ away, the lens's _____

point cannot be changed enough to keep the image there. As a result, the image gets blurry because the light is focused _____ of the retina. Because light is being refracted too strongly, a _____ lens can be used to correct this problem. When you are _____ , your eye's lens can adjust to objects far away, but it cannot focus on objects that are close. This is because the eye refracts light too _____ . A _____ lens must be used to correct this problem.

13 The cones in your retina are used to detect the _____ of the light you are seeing. Some cone cells are sensitive only to _____ -frequency visible light (red light), while others are sensitive to _____ - frequency visible light (green light), while still others are sensitive to _____ - frequency visible light (blue light).

14 The additive primary colors are _____ , _____ , and _____ . Television screens and computer monitors _____ these colors to make all the colors you see. Red and green, for example, add in equal parts to make _____ , while _____ and red add in equal parts to make magenta.

15 While the additive primary colors can add to make all the colors you see, the _____ primary colors are used for inks and paints. These three colors are _____ , _____ , and _____ . When equal amounts of yellow and magenta inks are mixed, for example, the result is _____ ink. When equal amounts of cyan and _____ inks are mixed, the result is _____ ink.

16 The colors we see from objects are a result of the wavelength of light that

_____ off them and hits our eyes. The dye that colors a shirt, for

example, uses the _____ primary colors to determine what

wavelengths _____ off the shirt and hit our eyes. As a result, if a blue

shirt is put in a dark room and magenta light is shined on it, the shirt will appear to be

_____ , since the blue dye reflects both cyan and magenta light.

If a yellow light were shined on the blue shirt in a dark room, it would appear

_____ .

MODULE 16 SUMMARY (OPTIONAL)

1 Although the sun is a _____ sequence star, there are several things that make it very _____ when compared to other stars in the universe. The vast majority of stars in the universe exist in _____ systems, where stars orbit each other. This would cause severe _____ changes in any planet that orbited such a system, making it extremely difficult for _____ to exist on any such planet. There are much bigger stars in the universe, but if the sun were as big as they are, it would _____ Earth in its orbit! In addition, there are stars that are smaller than the sun. However, if Earth were to orbit such a star, it would have to be_____ in order to get enough energy to support life. If a planet got that close to such a star, the large _____ forces it would experience would make it far too dangerous to support life. Of the stars in this general region of the universe, the sun is in the top 10% in terms of its _____ . The combination of the sun's mass and size, then, make it the _____ star to support life on Earth.

2 The sun is essentially a big ball of _____ and _____ gas. The part of the sun that we can see is called the _____ . Underneath that you find the _____ , and underneath that, the _____ . The deepest part of the sun, however, is its _____ , where nuclear _____ reactions turn _____ into _____ . Those reactions produce _____ , which is what makes the heat and light that the sun emits.

3 Every now and again, sudden and intense variations in the brightness of the

_____ occur. These variations are called _____ ,

and they send enormous amounts of energy to the earth in a short amount of time,

which can _____ satellites, radio communications, and even power

grids. Although the surface of the sun's photosphere is a place of violent activity, it is

"_____" compared to other, similar stars in the universe. Single stars

with roughly the same size and composition of the sun release solar flares that are 100 to

100 million times more _____ than even the most violent solar flares

that we have seen coming from the sun.

4 When a large nucleus is split into smaller nuclei, it is called _____ . This

process can result in a large amount of _____ , and it is the basis of

how nuclear _____ plants make electricity. When two or more small

nuclei fuse to make a bigger nucleus, it is called _____ , and that is

what powers the sun.

5 Nuclear fission reactions require a _____ and a large nucleus, and they

produce two or more smaller nuclei and several _____ . Because of

this situation, one nuclear reaction can start _____ nuclear reactions.

If there is a _____ mass of the large nucleus, this can lead to a

_____ . If there is a lot more than a _____ mass

of the large nucleus, the _____ can get out of control, resulting in a

nuclear explosion.

6 While nuclear power is reasonably cheap and will last a long, long time, it can be

_____ . A nuclear power plant _____ explode

because there isn't enough of the large nucleus to allow the chain reaction to get that

out-of-control. However, if the control systems fail, a _____ can occur,

which is what happened to the _____ nuclear power plant in the Soviet

Union in 1986. Nuclear fission also produces _____ byproducts, and

there is no clean way to dispose of them. Although nuclear fission can be dangerous and

polluting, it is not clear that it is any more dangerous and polluting than other forms

of energy production. Coal-burning power plants, for example, dump pollution into the

_____ , and coal mining has resulted in more than 100,000

_____ in the U.S. since 1900.

7 The _____ of a star is determined by the star's temperature. The

_____ of a star as it appears in the night sky is called the star's

apparent magnitude, while its _____ after being corrected for the

_____ from Earth to the star is its absolute magnitude. Plotting the

absolute magnitude of stars versus their temperature makes a

_____ , which is used by astronomers to classify stars.

8 On the Hertzsprung-Russell Diagram, the _____ stars form a roughly

diagonal band that goes from the upper left of the graph to the lower right of the graph.

_____ stars form a diffuse band at low absolute magnitudes and

various temperatures. _____ stars are found at low temperatures and

absolute magnitudes of about zero to -5. _____ stars are found at

high temperatures and high absolute magnitudes.

9 Main sequence stars are the most _____ in the universe. The

more massive a main sequence star is, the _____ its absolute

magnitude. White dwarves seem to be the next most _____ . They

are _____ and not very _____ . They are, however,

very _____ . Supergiants are the _____ stars in the

universe. They are very bright and seem to be _____ in the universe.

Red giants are _____ stars that are very bright. They produce their

energy by nuclear _____ , but it is different from the kind that takes

place in main sequence stars.

10 Stars with absolute magnitudes that change are called _____ , and there

are two main kinds: _____ and _____ .

_____ are exploding stars, the most extreme being

_____ , which expand rapidly and brighten enormously and then fade

away _____ . The debris left over from such an explosion is a cloud of

bright gases called a _____ . A _____ , on the other

hand, regularly expands and contracts without losing _____ .

This changes its _____ on a regular basis. One particular type of

pulsating variable, the _____ , is important, as it is used

to measure universal distances that are too long to be measured with the more precise

method known as _____ . _____ binary stars vary

in apparent brightness not because their absolute magnitude changes but because one of

the two stars can _____ our view of the other.

11 A light year is defined as the _____ .

Since light travels quickly, this is a very _____ distance.

12 A large ensemble of stars, all interacting through the gravitational force and orbiting

around a common center, is called a _____ . There are four main types:

_____ , _____ , _____ ,

and _____ .

13 Our galaxy, the _____ , is a _____ . Our sun

is on the inner edge of the _____ arm of that galaxy. Our galaxy is part

of a small group of about 30 galaxies, which is known as the _____ .

This group of galaxies is on the outer edge of a cluster of galaxies known as the

_____ .

14 The fact that light coming from distant galaxies has longer wavelengths than expected is

referred to as the _____ shift. Although it was once thought that this

was a _____ shift, it is now considered evidence that the universe is

_____ . Most astronomers think the universe is

_____ without a _____ . However, some think that

there is a _____ which is roughly marked by Earth's solar system. If this

is true, light from galaxies that are billions of light years away could have traveled to Earth

while just a few _____ years passed on Earth.

APPENDIX A
Lab Report Checklist

Objective

❏ You have explained what the problem or question is that you are trying to find out about.

Hypothesis

❏ Your hypothesis makes sense and you have explained why this is your prediction of what will happen (using the information you know about the topic). **(If/then statement)**

Materials

❏ Your materials list includes everything that you used for the lab.

❏ Your materials list includes quantities for each material when appropriate.

Procedure

❏ Your procedure paragraph clearly explains the steps you completed in the correct order so that anyone could repeat your lab EXACTLY.

❏ You have included safety tips and helpful hints so people won't make mistakes.

❏ You have made sure you are testing only one variable, and ALL of the others are kept the same when appropriate.

Data/ Observations

❏ Your measurements are accurate and include units (such as centimeters or seconds).

❏ You have put your measurements or observations into a scientific table, graph, or labeled picture.

❏ You have included every detail of what you saw happening (no inferences).

❏ You have shown any math work you did.

Results

❏ You have written a paragraph which explains what your data are showing (analyzed your data).

Conclusion

❏ You have used scientific vocabulary when possible.

❏ You have explained how the experiment relates to what you are learning in the text.

❏ You have explained how the lab answers the question for the lab.

❏ You have explained whether or not your hypothesis was supported by the data.

❏ You have identified and explained any possible sources of error.

Lab Report Grading Rubric

	Exceeding Standard (4 pts)	Meeting Standard (3 pts)
Objective/ Purpose and Hypothesis (if applicable)	• Purpose for the investigation is clearly stated. • Hypothesis is reasonable and includes an explanation, using relevant background information from the text.	• Purpose for the investigation is clearly stated. • Hypothesis is reasonable and includes a simple explanation, using some background information from the text.
Materials	• Materials list is complete.	• Materials list is missing 1 or 2 items.
Procedure	• Procedure is clear and presented in logical order for completion. • Procedure includes enough detail to make lab repeatable. • Includes safety tips and guidelines to avoid mistakes. • All variables are identified and controlled for except experimental variable.	• Procedure is clear and presented in logical order for completion. • Procedure includes enough detail to make lab repeatable. • Includes safety tips and guidelines to avoid mistakes. • Major variables are identified and controlled for except experimental variable.
Data/ Observations	• Data are accurate and include units. • Data are represented in an organized table or drawing. • Observations are detailed and complete. • Calculations are shown when appropriate.	• Data are accurate and include units. • Data are represented in an organized table or drawing. • Observations are complete. • Calculations are shown when appropriate.
Results	• Student goes above and beyond by summarizing results and identifying trends.	• Student adequately summarizes results.
Conclusions	• All appropriate scientific vocabulary is used accurately. • Direct connections between the experiment and text lessons are made. • Connects the question and hypothesis. • States whether hypothesis (when applicable) is supported by specific data. • Discusses/identifies relevant sources of error and how they could affect the outcome of the experiment.	• Most scientific vocabulary is used accurately. • Direct connections between the experiment and text lessons are made. • Connects the question and hypothesis. • States whether or not the hypothesis (or question, if there was no hypothesis) was supported by the data with specific evidence. • Discusses/identifies relevant sources of error.

Approaching Standard (2 pts)	Not Meeting Standard (1 pt)	Total Points
• Purpose for the investigation is stated. • Hypothesis is incomplete or does not include relevant background information from the text.	• Purpose for the investigation is not clear. • Hypothesis is irrelevant.	
• Materials list is missing 1 or 2 major items or several minor items.	• Materials list is missing several major and minor items.	
• Procedure shows some connection to the question. • Procedure is unorganized, lacks detail, or contains irrelevant information. • A few safety tips and guidelines are included. • Several major variables are overlooked.	• Procedure shows little to no relevant connection to the question. • Procedure is incomplete. • No evidence of controlling variables.	
• Some data are incorrect or missing units. • Data are represented in an organized table or drawing. • Observations are basic.	• Data and observations are missing or incomplete. • Data representation is unorganized.	
• Results summary is too brief or inconsistent with data.	• Results are missing or irrelevant.	
• Some scientific vocabulary is used but is not always accurate. • Makes vague connections between the experiment and text lessons. • Connects the question and hypothesis. • States whether hypothesis (when applicable) is supported by specific data. • No sources of error discussed or sources of error are not relevant.	• Science vocabulary is not used or not accurate. **Missing one or more:** • Direct connections between the experiment and text lesson. • Connects the question and hypothesis. • States whether or not the hypothesis (or question, if there was no hypothesis) was supported by the data with specific evidence. • Sources of error.	

APPENDIX B
Power Tools of Learning
by Debra Bell

Discuss it!

Define it!

Contrast it!

Connect it!

Analyze it!

Elaborate it!

Compare it!

Do you want to master your schoolwork more quickly and deeply? Do you want to be able to recall and use what you've studied whenever you need it? The learning strategies represented on this page will help you transfer your knowledge from short-term to long-term memory, where you can recall information at will.

Classify it!

Graph it!

These power tools make up the Study-Smart Student Toolkit and represent the kinds of mental operations (or deep thinking) you should engage in when studying.

1. Analyze it!
2. Classify it!
3. Compare it!
4. Contrast it!
5. Connect it!
6. Define it!
7. Discuss it!
8. Elaborate it!
9. Evaluate it!
10. Exemplify it!
11. Graph it!
12. Illustrate it!
13. Investigate it!
14. Model it!
15. Name it!
16. Organize it!
17. Question it!
18. Repeat it!
19. Transform it!
20. Use it!

Exemplify it!

Illustrate it!

POWER TOOLS
OF LEARNING

Find out how to use these power tools in each of your school subjects at www.studysmartstudent.com.
© 2011 by Debra Bell

Investigate it!

Evaluate it!

Model it!

Transform it!

Name it!

Organize it!

Question it!

Repeat it!

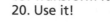

Use it!

NOTES

NOTES

NOTES

HERE'S YOUR NEXT YEAR OF SCIENCE!

EXPLORING CREATION WITH BIOLOGY
2nd Edition

After completing our award-winning Physical Science course, we recommend that the student take this course during the same year that he or she is taking Algebra 1 (typically the first year of high school). *Exploring Creation with Biology* is a college-prep biology course that provides a detailed introduction to the methods and concepts of general biology. With a strong emphasis on the vocabulary of biology, the course provides the student with a strong background in the scientific method, the five-kingdom classification scheme, microscopy, biochemistry, cellular biology, molecular and Mendelian genetics, evolution, dissection, and ecosystems. Please note that this course does not contain a discussion of human anatomy and physiology. (Most college biology professors do not consider human anatomy and physiology to be a part of a solid, college-prep biology course.) Anatomy is such a detailed subject that it merits an entire course (found in our book, *The Human Body*). In this text you will find:

- **CREATION-BASED SCIENCE**
- **CONVERSATIONALLY-WRITTEN AND ACADEMICALLY RIGOROUS TEXT**
- **EXPERIMENTS THAT ARE ENGAGING AND EASY TO PERFORM**
- **SUPPORT FROM OUR HELP LINE STAFFED BY APOLOGIA ACADEMY TEACHERS**
- **ACCESS TO ADDITIONAL ONLINE RESOURCES FOR MORE ADVANCED LEARNERS**

This is a two-volume set. The high-quality hardcover student text contains all student material, study questions, laboratory exercises, and module study guides with color photos and illustrations. The softcover solutions-and-tests manual contains answers to module study guides, tests, and test solutions. A booklet containing an extra set of tests is shrink-wrapped with the manual.

Author: Dr. Jay L. Wile and Marilyn F. Durnell
Format: Textbook with solutions manual
Prerequisites: None
Recommended Grade: 9

Full Course on 2 CD-ROMs
Companion CD-ROM
MP3 Audio CD

Additional instruction offered from APOLOGIA ACADEMY next page

Flash Card App for the iPad, iPhone, and iPod Touch

NEW!

Available on the App Store

Please consult the Apologia website for available lab materials

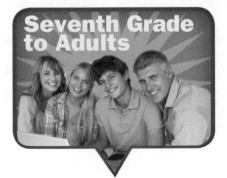

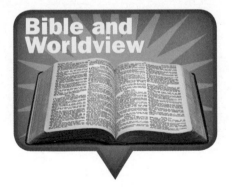